There's No Room

For

Jugglers in My Circus

By
J Cook

Pen Press Publishers Ltd

First published in Great Britain by
Pen Press Publishers Ltd
The Old School
39 Chesham Road
Brighton BN2 1NB

ISBN 1-905203-67-5
ISBN13: 978-1-905203-67-3

Printed and bound in the UK

A catalogue record of this book is available from
the British Library

Cover design by Jacqueline Abromeit

A bit of glamour with the reality shining through.

I hope you enjoy reading this book as much as I enjoyed writing it.

CONTENTS

"Some People Really Needed To Be Educated in the Ways of the Firm"

THE WOOD

I just sat down for a moment and found myself reminiscing about my past. I found myself back in the Manor. The Wood. Borehamwood.

It's the sort of manor you could drive through and you wouldn't know you'd even been there. The sort of place where you'd introduce yourself to one person, and before the end of the night the whole community would know what you were about, and what women you'd taken home that night. The sort of place where you could tell a pal something in secret and before you knew it, it might as well have been in the local paper, because everyone would know about it.

It was the sort of place where everyone was your friend to your face, but couldn't wait to stab you in the back with a comment or two, or use a bit of gossip you thought had long been buried but which came back to haunt you.

The place was like a magnet. Every time you tried to leave it, it would draw you back and you'd be trapped there. Or that's how it felt.

Then there were those who fell foul to the devil's dandruff (cocaine). These people that were your part time friends or more like acquaintances who, once you came to your last line, were nowhere to be seen, and had stopped following you to the toilets a long time ago, now they'd helped Hoover your last piece and knew you had no more left.

That's the place where I grew up. There was the odd good friend but no one you could trust your life, or your women with. Well, one or two, maybe.

THE HILL TOP DAYS

That's where we were sitting, on the hilltop where we used to hang out. Myself and a few friends, a motley crew you could say, as if we were 16 again. Young and free, that's how things seemed back then, or so we thought. No cares in the world, just sitting there with the girls and lads taking acid, speeding, watching the sunrise and the nights pass by. Staring into the stars with psychedelic images running through my mind, and magic thoughts and beliefs which meant nothing at all after you'd come down. They were just moments of madness, laughing at myself and each other. If people could have seen us, the men in white coats would have been sent out on our behalf. The only people that did come were the Old Bill now and again.

Things had no true meaning to me back then. I was just another Peter Pan in my own right, waiting for Wendy to come along. A few did, but we'll talk about them later.

Thinking of what life had to offer us, well to be honest, in the state we got ourselves into with the cocktails of mind-bending drugs we took every night the future seemed doomed, but who cared?. We were young and having fun. So much time passed by unnoticed. Other friends seemed to move on or settle down without us noticing. With a mind fuelled by drugs I was anyone I thought I could be or conjured up. I spent many years there in the Wood, and knew most people young and old. I also learned what the people were like and were about. Well, most people. Not everyone was like that, of course. Just a few people I seemed to meet, know or be around.

DAY DREAMING

Day dreaming of being rich and making my family proud, how wrong I was. That's where it all began, in so many words and endless drug talk. So in depth and so interesting you even started to believe your own bollocks and of course the bollocks your pals talked all made sense, but only to the listener, not to the talker who'd be lost in an intellectual trance brought on by the cocaine.

Then there were the pubs. I hated them, all full with jokers, comedians, drunks full of ego and bravado and thinking they were macho men. Thinking they could take on the world after a few beers, saying they'd done this and that. Proper clowns, but when the time came, when they upset someone it seemed all they could do was talk a good game. They'd always say they'd get this fella down or hide behind someone else's reputation, which turned out to be just a figment of their imaginations. As normal, as the beer took over, they talked about everyone else's business but their own. They were always chatting about that bird and this fella, but they never really knew anyone. They also bragged about the local slappers and how many beers they could drink before they'd take them home, or were asked home by them, knowing full well their fella wouldn't care because he was in the next pub doing the same, in the hope the slapper wouldn't find out.

That's why there was so much gossip the next day. It seemed everyone could have been related in one way because of all the partner swapping that went on. Even your pals would know more about your own bird than you did, or so it seemed. Those places weren't for me. I like honest people, not the actors, liars, and fakers that seemed to be in the pubs. Or the ones I seemed to attract, you know, the blaggers with their speeches. We've all met them. That's all the pubs had to offer me, but I had better things to catch up with. Or so I thought. I wanted to be around loyal people and have a good lady on my arm with morals and standards and a good honest head on her shoulders who'd be worth treating with respect and trust, not a slapper or cocaine prostitute that so many women had let themselves become. She wouldn't be like the Wendy's of before, but a proper lady you could trust to be around your pals. If one of them took a liberty and made a move on her she'd put them in their place and tell me what had happened, so I could have words with the rascal. And she wouldn't be some woman the police had planted without you knowing, as many a time they had with other criminals.

I guess the power of the devil's powder was too much even for them. Once it had hold of you, you were bang in trouble and your self respect started to take a back seat. As I was to find out for myself.

Only the small things in life are free, like good manners, respect, honesty, and love. Whatever you want in life apart from them things, costs. There's no such thing as a free lunch. Well, only if you stayed with a girl you'd picked up the night before and after the beer had worn off or you'd come down off the drugs, she still looked OK, and not like something out of a Halloween party, then you might stay long enough for her to knock you up a bit of breakfast the next morning, before you jogged on. Many a time it didn't work out like that. I'd take a woman home and take my beer/drug goggles off in the morning, roll over to give her a cuddle, and nearly jump 12 feet in the air with fright, because the gorgeous woman I was with now looked pretty scary. I'd think fuck! Where did she come from? Surely I didn't get into her ugly sister's bed by mistake? I wasn't no oil painting myself, but I know the difference between the nice and not so nice. I guess after 12 o'clock they all turn back, just like Cinderella did.

Sometimes I was lucky and did come away with a free breakfast, so it wasn't all bad. I guess with drink or drugs, and a head so smashed as it was back then you learned to take the rough with the smooth or you'd just go home alone because you always knew mum would cook up a bit of breakfast. Then I wouldn't have face the consequences of the Halloween women I'd come back with, hiding my pants in the hope that I would stay a bit longer in the morning because I'd been looking for them, or having to hand my phone number over and if I did it was always wrong, of course. Mum saved me many a night from the clutches of the unknown without even knowing. It's amazing, what's on the dance floor out there. I quickly learned not to put my drug glasses on. Until I knew the girl, or spent some time with her, then I didn't have to face the memories coming back to haunt me every time I looked in the mirror, or met up with old pals.

So with all that going on I needed to do what I did to pay for my habit and the crazy nights ahead of me. Otherwise where was I to get this money for the wasted years of mind-numbing uselessness that were yet to come my way?

MEETING MR B

That's when I first met this fella.

He came across as a man of principles, fixed in his ways. A smooth sort of James Bond looking character and a gangster by nature, as I was to find out. He dressed up in fine expensive clothes, all designer names, nothing less than Armani, Gucci and a few other suits that had been flown over from Milan for him. He looked as sharp, smart and as crisp as new bank notes, the day I had the pleasure of taking a bundle of them out of the Bank of England. He had a brand new polished executive motor that looked like James Bond's M had handed it to him, with loads of gadgets and an in car-phone which would have been proper large on the barge back then…..

We've all met some gangsters in our life, sometimes on good terms, and, those of us unlucky enough, on bad terms, and there's a bundle of books written by them and about them. This book is not about them, but about the way it might have been or the way things might have gone. I'm far from being any sort of gangster, but to be honest, I tried to play the game. But playing and being are like saying, 'I live on Earth, not far from the Moon'! I was just a desperate boy in a man's world, and I put myself in some desperate situations back then, or at least found myself in them. They weren't all bad ones, though. Some were good and some were bad. That's life. Some times you're up and some times you're down. You have to take the rough with the smooth.

We'll call this fella Mr. B. He was the sort of fella that oozed confidence in every situation he was in. A well built man, very stern and modest in his ways. And he was well liked, or seemed to be. He was an old timer. He'd done and seen a lot. He had many a story to tell of old that would make you unable to sleep at night and would put the frighteners on you, or scare you shitless till you filled your pants, but if he did tell you he'd probably have to kill you. That's if he was stupid enough to tell the tales in the first place. I doubt he would let them slip out because it would be more than his life he'd be giving away, more so his liberty banged up doing porridge somewhere. So there were some things that were best not asked or talked about, long done and long forgotten, but not by the people that had done the dirty deeds. They just pushed them to the back of their minds and went on with business as usual.

Mr B was around 40; still looking as well as the Queen's head does on a £50 note. He was very clean cut sort of fella. His hair always looked liked he had just stepped out of a salon; he was always so neat and well groomed. I'd say he knew his stuff and was wise in his ways. He knew the crack, and he'd done the circuit many a time. There was no pulling the wool over his eyes. He knew all the tricks in the book, and had pulled a few tricks himself out of the hat. Deep down, though, it was who had the biggest bluff at the end of the day? Or who had the manpower and money to pull things off if the bluff was called?

He was the ticket to my new ways, or so I thought. He was everything my messed up head wanted to be. You could say I looked up to the fella. In my sick mind I thought he would be a true friend and maybe one day, I hoped he would take me on as a partner, and do for me what I did for him.

Which was treating him with the upmost respect and showing him endless loyalty. But that was just a big dream for a little boy. In some ways he was like a father figure to me, or that's how I looked up to him, but sometimes he even failed me too, as you'll read later.

Maybe I failed him when the devil's dandruff started to take over and turned me into a liability as it has most players of this game, but I played the game the best I could and with the utmost respect and by the rules. He must have overlooked that, I guess. He had other things on his mind, like money. He had his mind on his money and his money on his mind you could say, or maybe he was too selfish to have noticed the respect I paid him.

Like most gangsters, they're always connected, and he was so much so that he had more connections and customers than British Telecom, whether in England or abroad. He always had women falling at his feet and people showing him endless respect. It was like he had a sort of VIP everywhere he went which I guessed came with the job. This was soon to rub off on me as we were seen together in the manor. Manors plus clubs and the odd restaurant. One in particular was the Indian in Leeming Road that served up top nosh to its customers and the utmost respect to us. Mr B never seemed to pay with cash or a credit card. It seemed he had a golden handshake with the bouncers, and then you were in the clubs. No queue, no pay, no worries, and at the bars a round of drinks was always accompanied with a free bottle of champagne brought to his table. He wasn't short of a few bob.

He gave the impression that he was cake a boo and probably not far off it, if the truth be known. People would be handing him money here, there and everywhere, but not the tickers. They wouldn't be because their debts were long overdue and most of them were now in hiding. They were under the illusion that once drugs or money was ticked or money was borrowed it didn't have to come back.

It's amazing what people, especially women, will do for a free drug plus a bit of importance, but underneath it all people were only respecting the drugs, not the person. Respect has to be earned and not through drugs. It comes with the person you are and the right sort of attitudes so there's a little less for the bullies out there. It weren't all what it was made to look like. If you opened your eyes wider and read between the lines, people were out to see what they could get for free, or how they could use you. It was hard to trust people 'cause they always had hidden agendas or alternative motives. It was like you were used as a pawn in a chess game, but the game weren't chess. It was real life. You'd have friends when you had powder around you but once it came on top and you were sent to jail and needed them, they seemed to disappear.

Also, you know the women batting their eyelids, showing a bit of leg and nicely dressed up in such a tight little dress, when you looked at them it seemed like you had x-ray eyes because you could see every single curve of their sexy looking hour-glass figure, with their nipples poking through. Also the dress would be so short that their tits were nearly falling out all over the gaff. The make-up so well done you'd think Van Gogh had put it on for them. They'd be going out of their way to walk in front of you, or past you and would be wiggling a cute looking botty in your direction for your eyes only. They'd wink, smile and giggle at you on passing, and then risk getting caught in the men's toilets squashed up in a cubicle next to you. Then they'd be leaning over the toilet seat to powder their nose with what you'd kindly donated for their troubles, and whilst leaning over to Hoover every last crumb of powder up, they'd be flashing you a naked peach of an arse, with a thong that would be nicely, tightly wrapped around it. Then after that they'd give you a little cuddle or kiss or they'd be all over you all night for a little line here and there for them and their pals. Once you'd fallen for their charm, you'd hand them a free cheeky half, never to see them til the next night when the games would begin again.

Then there was the geezers buying you drinks. They also thought that meant an invite to the toilets for a line or two here and there. Even they took liberties. The liberty takers, you know who you are! They'd keep the £50 note you had left rolled up for them in the toilets next to a big line of cocain that looked like a caterpillar and hope you had forgotten about it. A few times I had and they would try and swap the £50 for a £5 pound note and they or we wouldn't remember as we would all be well sniffed up. The liberty taking pals who when it was their time to show a little respect back, would whine, then put you out a line, not even big enough to give a hamster a headache. They never lost their notes because the amount of times they'd ask you for it, it might as well have been tied to their trousers with an elastic band, they were so scared of losing it. I'm not that sort of fella to take a man's note after he's had the decency to hand out a free bee line to me. That's the difference between the no good and me.

Then came the people who talked rubbish till you gave them what they'd
bought or ordered and then went on their way. It was all small talk, really, all bollocks about how they liked you, sweet mate. It seemed that while they were sniffed up, the only thing that came out of their mouth was a load of false shit. The sort of people that wouldn't give you the time of

day if you didn't have anything on you. There was the odd businessman or the odd banker who also liked the cocaine or a parcel of it here and there. Not forgetting the bent copper's or the odd C.P.S. that when you got raided with ten kilos in your house and you were up in court it turned into three in front of the judge. You knew some thing weren't right but what could you say? Just thank you, your honour The lawyers were in the game for some dirty money when they could get the offer. They knew what went on but it's hard to see the truth when you've got a fifty pound note rolled up next to a line that had their name written all over it with the villain slapping you on the back when the deal was done, thanks very much.

You'd be surprised the amounts of under cover addicts that are out there. (To say names would see a contract drawn up with my name all over it. Names are not important in this book). With the positions they were in you wouldn't blink twice at them, let alone know what went on behind closed doors. Them lawyers were partial to the odd back hander here and there, to get you out of jail and back on bail, so it was well worth it. If it had come well on top you could be landing in Spain before the papers landed on the Judge's desk. It was bon voyage and hello my amigo, but you couldn't run forever, unless you were an untouchable, but even a few of them got caught up with eventually. It seems your luck could run out at any time, as they'd found out now they were banged up. So sometimes it was best to take what the judge was handing out, because after all, you deserved it. Guilty you're 'onour!

You always seemed to have an invite to everyone's parties, as long as on your guest list was the devil and his dandruff, and e (ecstasy) was always welcome. If the drugs could have come on their own, you wouldn't have been invited because that's all they really wanted. It would always turn out a bit messy as some of the guests would owe you money or Mr. B, and the people who'd been ducking and diving you for a while, would be there and wouldn't know you had turned up. But now you were there it meant you had caught up with these people, (unlucky for some). They seemed to always turn up in the least expected places. They thought that once they had ticked something off you that you then turned into the invisible man. They hoped they wouldn't see you again. Big mistake. We all live in the same world, so the odds are some day they'll be seen again or some one will know where they are.

When you asked these people for the money they owed, they would come out with an unbelievable story you'd think they were standing in the dock at court trying to convince a jury. You always caught up with people even in the dole queue when it was their payday or when they least expected it, otherwise they were like Houdini and would do his disappearing act and would be nowhere to be seen until a few quid was flashed about to their pals and then they'd bubble them up and tell where they could be found or were hiding. It's like a neighbourhood watch but on the streets or at street level. You may get a cash reward if you uncover the hiding place of a tickers.

Then the parties would really go off with a bang. The non-payers banging off the end of a fist. "Some people really needed to be educated in the ways of the Firm". People never really seemed to learn till they were sitting in casualty, or had a few holes put in them. Funny, after that the money and the arrangements seemed to arrive on time without having to go out of your way to hunt it down or to find the people to get the money back.

So things weren't all as good as they seemed. It was dog eat dog, and I was in a dog's world. That's the real reason why they didn't like you to be there at the parties. They hoped that it would be cocaine on tap without paying. Well, it was for close friends. Everyone likes a party animal and a few of Mr B's firm were proper animals, but no-one likes a party pooper when an ambulance has to be called to take away the no good tickers for debts long overdue. Not forgetting the people who thought you had money that grew on trees, because they'd speech you with a sort of "you're knocked" ending but as usual it all ended in tears. Not for us, of course, but for them and an extra monkey would be added to their debts for our time. No one likes being held upside down in a chair with two big chimps while their toes are being blow-torched cause they seem to go soft and gooey on the inside and crunchy, and crispy and swollen on the outside. When the old saying was said to them "Say hello to my little friend Scar face, the Harry hooter (shooter)", you could have been a mime artist with that because they knew what was coming next so the money seemed to turn up the next day, or at least a day or two later, never too late because they knew they might be pushing up the daisies. They never seemed to realise it wasn't your money. It was one of the bigger firm's money they were spending or sniffing.

It was always some else's money. There's always someone further up the ladder who you paid or would have to answer to. No matter who you are or think you are. No one likes their money being spent and definitely not by someone else, only if it's by someone well high up on the ladder who it would be owed to, maybe one of the untouchables who I'd be paying the money to. So when they wanted their money from you there were no stories to

15

tell about where it was or how I was to get it. They didn't want to hear that. There's no excuse in this game. They've listened to many a story and excuses before and always replied with a story of their own which would always make more sense to me than the one I could come up with to stall them for a couple of days before I could get their dough sorted as I always did back then. Their story would go something like this: "THE LAST FELLA THAT TOLD A STORY ABOUT OUR DOUGH WE KINDLY HAD CONCRETE BOOTS MADE TO EXACTLY THE RIGHT SIZE FOR HIS FEET. THEY MADE ONE SIZE THAT FITS ALL, WHICH WAS HANDY AND WHICH WAS MOST KIND OF US, CONSIDERING THE SITUATION WE WERE PUT IN AND FOR SOME STRANGE REASON HE FELT THE NEED FOR A SWIM DOWN IN THE RIVER THAMES".

I guess it gets a bit hot when you've got two big chimps breathing down your neck for payments long overdue. So I'd think twice about their story next time before I told any. They would also say "YOU'D THINK HE WOULD HAVE TAKEN HIS BOOTS AND CLOTHES OFF AND TAKEN A SNORKEL WITH HIM". Then they'd all laugh and say "IF I DIDN'T GET THEIR DOUGH ON TIME OR ON DEMAND OR AS ARRANGED, THEN I'D BE THEIR NEW STORY TO TELL THE NEXT PERSON THAT THOUGHT THEY COULD TELL A STORY ABOUT WHY THEIR DOUGH WAS LATE OR WHY IT HADN'T TURNED UP AT ALL AND IT WOULD START WITH A MAN FOUND IN EPPING FOREST ON THE NEWSPAPER HEADLINES". The knockers never realised that if they didn't pay the firm, they'd be coming to see their family. So when a few good friends of mine had put some of the big knockers in wheelchairs, it was always too late for their apologies. It didn't matter about the money after that. It was more about the principle of the matter.

Like most gangsters, they have their fair share of enemies too, more so than the normal Joe Bloggs. Mr. B had James Bond mannerisms about him that went well with his image. Also you had to be like a secret agent just to keep one step ahead of the Old Bill or at least keep them on their toes. Before long I'd got myself mixed up in the whole image of things. Some day that would be me, so I set out to do them things and try to be like Mr. B the best I could. I'd watch and listen and see and learn a few tricks off him, some sort of code of practice that the faces and villains seemed to communicate by, work by or understand. Sometimes I'd get things wrong which would wind him up or I'd turn up late and the old saying would come up when he phoned "WHERE ARE YA?"

I'd reply, "I'M TEN MINUTES AWAY FROM YA". I could understand why he got a bit upset cause being on time was the difference from getting nicked or not when he was like a sitting duck waiting for me to turn up. I wanted a piece of the action, and what went with it. NOT REALLY KNOWING WHAT I HAD GOT MYSELF MIXED UP IN, but it was a way to pay off my own debts and habit and not be like the low lifes that were now robbing old ladies etc. Doing the things I done meant that I wouldn't be falling foul to the same thing or to the chimps when they were kicking down my door for debts long overdue. Normal people wake up with coffee and breakfast and the paper to look at, not with the door being kicked off and a shooter pushed in to your head or with ten Old Bill coming round for the morning raid.

So I started to do things as the firm did. If you can't beat them, join them. I went out my way to get a piece of the action, so before long I was up and working with a few tricks of my own and my own little firm. Which consisted of the good Treeny, the bad Bones, the ugly Lee and me, the Diplomat. Lee was not ugly in his looks but in his actions to others. The Diplomat was me and that's how I went about my business, with diplomacy. Also with what I'd learned off Mr. B and how he went about his daily business rounds and duties. Also not forgetting the minder I was given back then from one of the bigger firms to help collect money in. He was Big Wheel Will from Potters bar, he was one of three henchmen that I had on loan. He would have done any one or anything for me now that's respect.

I LEARNED THAT THERE ARE THREE SORTS OF GANGSTERS...

I've been in the company of known and unknown gangsters, faces and villiains, but for my own safety names are not important.

Along my way I was unlucky and lucky to meet three types of gangster.

NUMBER 1
The Real McCoy

These gangsters were everything the word gangster means. Proper dangerous people, all firm handed and well connected. They always kept their word and would be loyal in their ways. They lived by standards, morals and a code of practice that the faces of old had passed on down through time. They live by the sword, and died by it. They were old school. Sometimes they were family men who were treated with respect and didn't need to demand it, and sometimes they were loose canons who wouldn't think twice about putting a bullet in you. These gangsters earned their right to be well up on top in their league by doing what a gangster does best. They were true untouchables, a law unto themselves. Some were known and some preferred not to be because if you didn't know the enemy, how could you get to him? They were true members of any firm they worked for. When they gave you their word they would follow it right through to the very end. No questions asked. They'd work alone or for a firm, or firms, where the police worked for them and not them working for the Old Bill.

Not to mention that they seemed to have the odd C.P.S. wrapped up in their pockets, a few bent lawyers and banks and the odd accountant. A very few lucky ones had the odd customs officers who looked after them too or who could pull some string for them. That's how they knew the Old Bill were bringing in criminals and dangling drugs at them for info when entrapments were set up. Which meant they could clue people up with what to say to their advantage when they sent in one of their bent lawyers to get them off or find any little hole in the case and make it a bigger one. They lived in a proper dangerous world. They also rubbed shoulders with the flying squad now and then as some had grown up in the army together. They lived in 'THE UNDERWORLD'. Which to those of you who are reading this, I would not recommend. A world where action spoke louder than words and money did their talking for them. When things got messy the heavies were called in to do all their sweeping up, which was proper dirty work sometimes. Their hit men seemed to have permanent contracts already written up with the undertakers. They were connoisseurs at the disposing of bodies

They were the true gangsters and villains. Some were proper gentlemen and could be trusted and some were pure animals with no heart who'd be willing to tear your head off at any moment. These people made things happen. There's three types of people in this game they are the Thinkers, the Doer's and the Talkers. The thinker thinks about doing it the talker talks about doing it and the doers just do it. They didn't just talk about it. They done it and talked later. Also they all understood and respected the Queensbury rules. Well, some did, most of the time. The main rule was **If you used our money you must pay it back.** Simple, really. Why so many people got it wrong I don't know. They paid the price in the long run.

NUMBER 2
The Good Old Police Pet

Then there was the gangster number two, half gangster, half police pet. On one side of the coin he played the gangster. On the other side he only played it by the police rules cause of some deal they'd made when sitting in front of Customs and Excise or Scotland Yard or Flying Squad or the main CID boss or someone who could pull strings in the ranks. When they were pulled in they handed a few names of the firm they worked for, or from other firms they knew and said that they could arrange a deal where they worked for the Old Bill, and before long they were back on the streets after doing a couple of weeks, so it looked good on the outside but not on the inside. These gangsters didn't have Old Bill sewn up in their pocket cause they were now sewn up in the police pockets themselves, and on their books. They'd always get called back once the police dangled the carrot in their faces again or they wanted someone off the street or they were unlucky to get caught again.

They were gangsters who'd tell every one that you were no good. Or a shit cunt, mind my French, or a scumbag. But if they looked in the mirror, staring back at them would be a proper toilet rat. With the truth coming back into their face to haunt them because it was people's lives they were playing with.

There were no true winners or loyalties there; there was only the Old Bill that would also jump on the bandwagon and play at being the gangster themselves. To get info of other firms or to break down a protection racket that was getting out of hand, or get the Vice Squad in to stop other organisations setting up brothels and other no good things. They'd say to the police pet "Continue to work with us or go to jail. Simple rules or we'll let the word go out on the street to other firms to let them know what you're all about". It was no skin off their nose.

Of course they didn't want that going out on the grapevine, because if that was the word on the street it would be more than their lives were worth. They'd be pushing up the daises or well out of business and would definitely need witnesses protect then. If you couldn't do the time, they shouldn't have done the crime. Not do the crime and tell the police all the time, eh boys? Do your bird with pride and soldier on!

They never got a pension only witness protection. Proper Bertie Smalls, the no good grasses.

NUMBER 3
The Good Old Plastic Gangster

He'd learned all the mannerisms. Had the fake Rolex watch and the moody gold plus the leather jacket he got down the local market with some other fake labels. He knew all the faces, but no faces knew him. The only people that did know him were the people he had to make aware he was a gangster, but only now and then, if he could get away with it.

Others seemed to talk the talk but couldn't walk the walk. He made every effort to tell people that he was one.

He was a wannabe. He seemed to try to demand respect or made more noise than necessary so he got noticed. He'd walk to the front of a club and speak to the bouncer, asking him the time. Out of ear shot of course, and then he'd come back and say "Sorry, sweetheart. My friend ain't on the door tonight" (or any night if the truth was known), "so we've got to pay and queue up." Well it looked good and maybe impressed a few tarts once or twice. These plastic gangsters were far from being Big Potatoes. As the Old Bill would say, they were "small fish in a big pond". Pond life. Proper mackerels, more like Del boys. They did any little dirty work to get noticed or recognised by the bigger firms or players.

So sometimes these plastic gangsters would get their moment of fame because they'd be used as tools to clear the roads for the big boys. Well we've all had to start somewhere.

To be a true gangster you're born one or the family are already members, or you're taken under someone's wing and you learn the ropes. Or you're well connected, or come very highly recommended by other criminals or villains. Or just unlucky, to be in the wrong place at the wrong time with the wrong type of company.

MEETING MR B. PUTTING YOUR NECK ON THE LINE....

It was night time, about half eight. I was with a good friend of mine called Elaine. She was really a friend of a friend, and an agony aunt as I'd share my troubles and problems with her. She was Sam's best friend, you know, one of the Wendy's I talked about earlier. Anyhow, Sam caused me so much pain back then that being a man of my qualities, if I'd been beaten in a fight or hurt by the enemy I'd just brush it off or go back for seconds once I was better to put the liberty taker in his place. But hurt a man's heart and it's like throwing a jigsaw puzzle of a broken heart on the floor and trying to put the pieces back together. When you find out a piece is missing, that's the piece that hurts the most.

So when a friend is involved, one that you've shared good times and secrets and trusted and treated like one of the family, also who you've treated with respect and kindness, it makes the pain that more powerful. That's where the saying "they take kindness for weakness" comes, and this friend had taken more than that. He took my women as well. The only good thing that come out of seven years that I spent with Sam was a beautiful daughter called CHELSEA, WHO I'LL CHERISH TILL THE DAY I DIE, AND ALWAYS WISH I COULD HAVE SPENT THEM LOST YEARS WITH. THE YEARS LOST THROUGH

NO FAULT OF MY OWN, I MIGHT ADD ONLY THE TWO YEARS THAT I SPENT DOING TIME.

Me and Elaine was just talking in her bedroom. Nothing fancy was going on that night, or any night with Elaine. We were just friends. There was a lot of cars tooting outside her window. When she looked out it was two of her older pals. (Elaine was also older than me by three years - I was nineteen then). The two geezers in the car asked her to come out. All excited she told me to come with her. As we went out parked up right next to her house was a brand new Escort XR3I. In their day they were smart motors to have. As we opened the doors to get in, a big mushroom cloud of smoke came out to greet us with the sound of Ratpack. I'd met the man a few times at the Venue when he came to the raves that were held there and also at Camden.

Once I'd met my old school friend there. Joel Samuels was his name. His dream came true because he is now DJ Luck. I met him again in 2004 at Ayia Napa when I was out there on holiday and business with the most beautiful woman I have ever met inside and out and who I had the pleasure of spending so many more good times with. Her name is Viv. Joel was spinning his decks with the magic of his songs he'd produced. You may know them as "A little bit of luck" and "No one does it better". I also met up with DJ Luck back home in Watford in Area nightclub, which was most pleasant.

Now the sounds were thumping from the system from inside the car. The two geezers were smoking weed and the car was full of smoke. We were in the back. They turned the music down, turned round and started to talk. They were so stoned they looked Chinese. I was passed the joint of weed and started to tote on it. Within seconds I too could feel my eyes go Chinese and couldn't get this stupid smirk of my face. It gave a new meaning to the Cheek and Chong films I used to watch back then. Now I knew why they acted like they did in the films.

Elaine asked, very inquisitively, how these lads could afford the motors because five days ago they didn't have two bob to scratch their arses with. With that the driver lent forward and said, "I've got one too in the same colour", then continued to tell how they'd managed to get the dough. Thinking I wasn't listening he leaned forward to Elaine's ear. Believe it or not two nights ago they were breaking into some garages in some manor when they'd stumbled on a stash of fifty two keys of the finest skunk weed that was about in that time, or at least in England. They couldn't believe their mince pies at what they'd found, as it's not every day you stumble on something like that, so without wasting any more time staring at it, they loaded it in to their clapped out van with a few other bits they could get their thieving little hands on. With that they went out of the manor so that no one would know it was them. They took it straight up to a dealer they knew in Luton and sold it cheap but not so cheap as to not be able to buy these motors for themselves, and still have some more money to collect off the dealer in a day or two.

Although I'd heard it all it didn't mean much to me then. These fellas were pretty lucky to find such a stash but unlucky they told every one. So I thought no more of it and continued to smoke the rest of the joint and just started to melt into the back seat a bit further. I told the fellas I had some speakers and a bass tube for sale, and they said they'd come and look tomorrow night at about 9pm. With my eyes feeling so heavy that they were hard to keep open and the hairs on my neck starting to stand on end, everything started to spin round and round. Then the hot and cold sweats came. I felt all hot and bothered like a wet lettuce. Before long they drove me home, I said goodbye to Elaine and bye to the fellas.

Just in time. As I got out the car and they drove off out it came, Hughie all over the floor and all over my shoes, my first whitey. I looked up and my vision was like a fly's and my head was buzzing like a wasp's. How could people smoke such shit, I thought. From that day on I knew that wasn't for me. I've had the odd one here and there and never really drunk unless I'm in the company of women, but I've never smoked a whole joint to myself.

So I wouldn't be needing an ambulance to straighten me out. I made it inside to the cupboards, pulled out biscuits and crisps and laid down on the bed. It was lights out. I was in a stoned comer.

I woke up the next morning to my door being banged on. When I opened the door it was my friend back then. We'll call him Rich. Rich came in and started chatting about how we still owed the local dealer money for the speed we'd had a few nights ago, so as usual I searched my room to see what I could give to the dealer for payment, and if we would be able to get some more. I'd nearly sold everything in my bedroom by now, as this was the only way I could get the money together. So we picked up my stereo and walked it to the dealer. He welcomed it with open arms and we got a few bits extra, which was a result. Rich paid off his part. That's why I called him Rich.

On the way back the phone rang and a loud angry voice said, **"Where are you?"** Rich said that he would be at my house in ten minutes. With that we arrived at my gaff and parked up out side was a brand new executive's motor with Mr B sitting in it. He told Rich to get in the motor and said a friend of mine had been done and he needed me at home.

And off they went. I went into the house and phoned Rich to see what all the drama was about. It turned out that Mr B's friend's garage had been broken into. "Rich", I said, "tell him to come round to mine. I might be able to help".

Within ten minutes Mr. B arrived. I opened the door and he walked straight in and before I could say anything, he said in a deep husky voice with daggers coming out his eyes, **"What do you know, son?"** He looked in a right state; I guess I would if I'd just lost all that stuff too. When the fella phones for it what do you say? "Well someone's had it?" By the look on Mr B's face he didn't want to tell the fella what had happened, because it was someone's much further up the ladder than him, by the sound of it all. He knew the currency was money not excuses.

"Well", I said, all proud of my self and sticking my neck out for him which seemed a regular thing after that, "I know who's got it."

"Where it is and who took it?"

Mr B was now very impressed just as I'd hoped. I also told him they'd be coming to my gaff tonight. He was over the moon. Well. so would I be if I knew my stuff was coming back. Mr. B left and the fellas turned up at 9 pm. We walked to my garage and I started to show them the speakers when out of the darkness four fellas appeared with balaclavas on and before you knew it the garage thieves were gone. Next day Mr B came round and thanked me for my troubles and handed me a gram of the devil's dandruff and £50. "Is that all?" I thought. I'd just saved him from more a less pushing up the daisies and that's all I got for my troubles. Well, back then I just wiped my mouth knowing now I was on the firm, or so I thought. Now I could ask for what I wanted. So before long, I was up and working for Mr B. Parcels were ticked and coming faster than Parcel Force, so now every day seemed like a Champagne Super Nova day.

Before long, life was taking a down hill slide. I now knew what Noel Gallagher meant when he sang, "Chained to a mirror and a razor blade". I was just finding out, because now I was becoming a slave to the devil's dandruff myself which wasn't Mr. B fault, as I was sniffing more and more as the days went past. I was up and working and was being seen with Mr B.

Before long I was trusted to take his nice little woman, the gangster's moll, out clubbing with her mate. At his request, which would turn out to be most weekends and which I didn't mind doing, as it was pleasant to go clubbing with two nice women on each arm. That's all they were, I might add, before anyone signs a death warrant for me. He'd have other business to deal with or be out with pals and there were certain business meetings where women weren't welcome, because you shouldn't mix business with pleasure. With his woman being with me he knew I'd keep an eye out for her, not that she needed it and sometimes it was the other way round. Both women would always go out their way to be nice and help me out as best they could of the dilemmas I'd get in to now and then.

Now Mr B's moll was a nice person with a kind heart. She helped me out many a time and we became good friends. She knew the crack, as Mr. B had trained her well, and of course she added her own special magic touch to the job. Before long it seemed to just come natural to her. Many other women find it hard to deal with or accept the pressures of what comes with being a gangster's moll. Some crumble under pressure or give up and just go mad, and some take their own lives, or run off with the Old Bill or someone up high in bigger leagues. Or move on to witness protection.

We would all go Bagley's, one of the best clubs in London. The two women and me had many a good nights at this club. With time, I got to know some of the security, one in particular was a girl, and we'll call her Sue. Sue would greet us when we came into park the car, and would ask if we could come in free on the radio without queuing up and several times she was nice enough to be able to do that for us, which was very nice of her. A few times after the club I would take her home as she lived in the same manor as we did. I only knew Sue for a short time, about two years, but in the time I did know her, we shared some good times together and a few laughs and she always went out her way to show me a little respect before she sadly passed away, God rest her soul...

A few times I would also go up to Bagley's with a friend and an acquaintance of mine. We'll call them Bones and Bonzo. I met Bones in Stonebrighed while I was over there doing a bit of work and we've been good pals ever since. This mad night, we were there at Bagley's. I had left with a nice looking woman who after twelve o'clock changed in to one of the Halloween girls we talked about earlier. We were just sitting in the car, rushing off the E's and chatting, snuggling up to each other with a blanket wrapped around us when Bones turns up on the scene and says, "where's Bonzo?"

I replied "With you I thought". Then all of a sudden Bonzo comes walking out towards the car just in his trousers. Now this was the weirdest cause. When he went in he was fully dressed, his eyes were the size of tunnels and his hair and his jaw were bouncing around so much he looked like he had just been electric shocked. He jumped in to the back of the car as if he wasn't aware that he was just in his trousers. All concerned, I said "Bonzo, what's happened mate?"

He looked at us with eyes rolling back in his head and his body all hunched forward because the effects of the E's. He then said, "Got any more E's?", with his lips moving all over the place before the words came out, like in a Chinese movie. Well, we all burst out laughing and so did he. He clearly had had enough and I felt responsible for him. I wasn't handing any more freebies out cos I was struggling to stay above board with eating so many myself and looking out for them, and I knew and could see for myself that he had enough, anyhow.

I threw the blanket to him to wrap himself around in. Bones went to look for his clothes, but no joy. So we then drove home and chilled out back at one of their houses till it was light and then being all paranoid going home in the morning or afternoon when we had finally all come down. It was a proper mad night. Mad because we'd been eating E's likes Smarties and you could die just on one. Things were getting well out of hand back then with the amount of drugs we were eating and the sleep we were missing. I even had to sell my car in the end to meet the payments for what we were all using.

Bones, his girl, a girl we'll call Lisa, and me would also go to Camden and other clubs. The club scene had come along fast and we would go most weekends. We would be there raving and rushing our tits off. You had to be at a rave to appreciate it: every one rushing, happy, loved up and with faces pulled with each rush. "got any more? You're my mate, you are". I'd just like to add that Bones' girl and Lisa would have helped me out with anything back in those days if they could, which didn't go without me appreciating it, especially Lisa introducing me to some of her bouncer pals from the Gas club in London where she worked on the door herself. This also helped me where paying was concerned, getting in to the strip club now and then with the manager's agreement of course. We would all go to Camden Palace and sometimes with the girls who were staying in the hostel in The Wood.

Camden was also a good club. Lisa would be dressed in a short white dress and looked like the Snow Queen. Bones' woman was dressed in a short pink dress and was the Lady in pink. She also looked like a Barbie doll. They loved clubbing and were still looking good and had plenty of energy. At the ages of thity and twenty eight at they could outdance us back then. They loved going clubbing with us and were proper little ravers. Two blondes dancing next to you, shaking and gyrating their sexy, sticky, sweaty bodiess to the banging garage beats. You couldn't ask for much more and the atmosphere was out of this world. We had some good nights clubbing, back then. The nights left me with some good memories, and I hope with the others too.

Me and Bones on a few occasions would go up to Camden Palaces on our own. We would spend the whole night raving, and getting rid of the odd one or two E's here and there. At one time Bones and me were like shadows. Where I was he was, and where he was I was. He was treated like one of the family by my parents just as other friends were, and the same with them and their families. That you'll hear about later.

We turned into E heads back then and would be with each over every day. We would be off our heads most days on whatever we had. I guess things did get a bit much for him. He saw how messed up I was getting on the drugs so he went on his own way to save his own sanity, which I couldn't blame him for. That was a long way before the end of this book but we still remained friends. We would be chauffeured. driven up in a brand new sports XJX Jaguar. It was silver metallic and the inside was all leathered up. It moved along like a purring lion. It had a baseline coming from it that was so crisp that you'd have thought Mozart was conducting it. You could hear us coming just before we drove past. It was definitely a head turner and it did turn a few heads, and worked wonders with the ladies. They seemed to love getting in it and sitting on our laps when we were giving them a lift back from the club, and would always comment on what a nice motor it was. We get used to beeping the horn for their friends so they could be seen in it and show off a little. Also it helped get us an invite back to their place where the early morning cocaine sniffing and more E popping would continue well in to the next afternoon. Which was costing me a bomb, and of course the odd wild sex here and there. If we were really lucky, that would put a good night to an end and give you a maximum boost till the next weekend arrived, when the raving and partying would continue all over again.

The motor belonged to a friend of mine from a different manor. As you can imagine we would be giving it Charlie large in it, driving round London to the clubs smoking joints out the window and rushing of the E's. It gave the impression that we were big potatoes, but we were far from big potatoes if the truth be known, but with a £40,000 motor, a 21 year old, 25 year old and the driver being 28 and a body builder and also getting into the club free. I guess we looked the part, and it did wonders for our egos and of course we didn't tell them that the car was his old man's, and the endless supply of drugs we were all taking were ticked by me and that I was desperately trying to sell more, to find the money for us to take more. To Bob we were not big potatoes but there were still nights to remember. How could you forget nights like that, no matter how messed up you were? There's some things you can't forget and those times were some of them. Any one that's had a night out at a club or rave would know how good they were back then, them nights rushing off the pills and garage tunes and the atmosphere that went with the whole club scene.

WE'LL CALL HIM THE ICEMAN AND HIS CRONEYS...

Well now, in between clubbing every weekend, I was working all over the manor for Mr. B, you could say. I was now one of his front line men, a foot soldier. Which meant I'd be selling drugs at street level, to any one that wanted them. I wasn't no drug pusher as people phoned me and asked me if I could get them, not force them to have them. Now I would always be putting my neck out on the line and look out for him and his family in more ways than one, and would remind people to sort out their long overdue debts that they owed him when I could. Also I would run little errands and deliveries for him here and there.

When his own blood, or friends of his own blood would nick jewellery, money, drugs or clothes from him, it was always me, the one to find out where they'd gone and who they'd been sold to so he could get them back, which he did. I guess I done that out of respect for him. After all, it weren't my drama. Many a time it caused me a great deal of strife back then which I shrugged off, but I would do it out of respect for Mr. B. Now and then I stopped other firms setting up in the manor, or would make Mr. B aware of them if they were out of my league.

Whilst working my evil trade I started to get messages, that I now was treading on someone's toes. But how could I be? This was Mr. B's manor. Everyone knew that and

35

that he had it sewn up. So how did this worm come out the wood work? Well it turned out that Mr. Iceman was running the other half of the manor, unknown to me. Something Mr. B had failed to mention? Or maybe he wasn't aware of it. Well, I was working my evil trade all over the manor, with better devil's dandruff and cheaper prices, which really didn't impress Mr Iceman one bit. So it wasn't long before people was telling me that Mr Ice wasn't a happy man and that if I continued to work in these parts he would teach me a lesson by shooting me. I told Mr B about it and he told me not to worry. "People don't tell you they're coming to shoot you son. You just get shot, so sounds like he's bluffing you. Sometimes in this circus it's all about who has the biggest bluff or the biggest balls to come and do what they say they're going to do. There's a lot of talk in this game without any actions and a lot of empty promises to go with it."

So I carried on with business as normal, that was until the night I was at my mum's, sitting there with one of the Wendy's and a nice one at that. Next thing that happened was my uncle comes in covered in blood and a fat lip. He was in a right state. They had proper set about him and left him in a bad way. "What happened to you?" I said.

Whilst mum was cleaning up his face, In a sad frightened voice he said, "You'd best stop doing what you're doing because you're going to get shot if you don't stop treading on Mr Ice's toes." He'd been roughed up pretty badly as a warning for me.

I asked, "Where and how did this happen to you?"

He replied that he was sitting in the pub and someone overheard that he was my uncle. So before long he was invited back to some bird's house where Mr. Ice and his cronies were. Then they started to rough him up and afterwards said to tell me that it was a little warning from them.

With that I asked where they were!

He told me, and I was off in the car faster than a bullet leaving a gun. Just as I started the engine up the mobile rang. It was then Happy, then a pal but he soon became a acquaintance when one night he'd got off his nut on crack and as it drove him mad with each lick as it does, came up with a story that I had slept with his woman, which he thought that meant he had the right to come and scare my mum to half to death by smashing her windows.

After I'd caught up with him by hunting him down in all the pubs, and playing cat and mouse, it seemed he wanted to say sorry and pay my mum back for the damage he'd caused. Rightly so, which I thought was fair enough with a little persuasion from me and a smart little manoeuvre from my driver back then, who was Mr. M when he cut him off in the BMW, which was most handy when he tried to do a runner from me. I had two drivers back then, or people that didn't mind driving me around. The other one was a nice blonde girl called Nosher. My driver Mr. M was good for driving me round London when I needed to meet friends and discuss business arrangements, as he knew it like the back of his hand and could more or less find the places I needed to be with his eyes closed. Which came in handy when I met a nice blonde Wendy once while we stayed in London doing some work. I'm sure he'll remember that night but that's a another story. You might hear about it in my next book, if this one does well. I guess if you put your mistakes right there's no need to cry over spilt milk but if you don't put the liberties right you bring whatever trouble comes with that liberty on yourself. If you put your mistakes right there's no need to be 'EDUCATED IN THE WAYS OF THE FIRM'.

How could he have thought that he could disrespect me like that? After all, he knows that I think a man's woman is his gold. Also that's how I'd expect any woman of mine to be treated back. I've got higher standards than to sleep with a friends' woman, but one man's gold could be another man's poison. Even if I was given the come on by them, which happened a few times, I still wouldn't entertain it out of respect for my pals, even if I wanted to, as he knew. If you don't have some morals and standards what do you have? Very little, I guess. The drugs had messed with his mind too. Well what else do you expect from drugs? In life there's only certain things you can take with you when you die and that's your morals, standards and loyalties, as well as your soul.

Happy said "Listen, I've just had the Iceman here. He's kicked off the door with a couple of cronies. I've got my missus and kid here and he's roughed me up in front of them, and they're petrified."

I said "Don't worry. I'm on my way to you. Stand outside your house. We've got business to attend to."

I arrived, picked Happy up, and we were off like bloodhounds hunting the fox. But as normal the fox had come on the scene and now had disappeared again. We searched the manor for him but he was nowhere to be seen. So we called it a night.

When I got home the threats that he wanted to shoot me played tennis with my mind. In my mind I was losing the game with every serve back but I needed to win the serve so I could sever him up and stop him coming for me and stop the threats to my family and friends. So much so, that I phoned a good friend of mine over in Mill Hill, who owed me a little favour, so arrangements could be made for me to have a Harry Hooter sorted out for my dramas.

The next morning, I was up early straight up to see my good friend to pick up the piece, but when I got there he told me that he hadn't ordered it for me, much to my regret. Also that he thought it would be best for me not to go round the manor like Clint Eastwood just yet, thank God. He then said not to worry 'cos there were more ways to skin a cat.

With that he said if I done him with my hands I'd probably get more respect. Queensbury rules. I guess he had a point there, because anyone stupid can pull a trigger but you don't want to kill a man unless it's necessary 'cos you can kill a family too with that and part of your self dies inside too, if you're the one that pulls the trigger. I was far from wanting to kill a man or hurt a family because of my actions. I'm a firm believer in what comes around goes around, and it was coming round to him real quick. Always does in the end, but then it came to me he would have a gun, or would he? He'd shown me a bullet from the car window once when driving by and told me it had my name on it. I didn't stick around to have a look to see if it had.

Anyhow I left my good pals with a small looking box, which was far from being any sort of Magnum 45. It turned out to be a stun gun, which shot out gas too, so at least now he would live to tell the tale. One lucky shot with this while he held the gun at me or tried to get it out and I would be all over him like a rash while he was shitting sparks. It seemed fair.

As I got back in to the Wood, Bingo was there crossing the road in front of me. He was one of Mr. Ice's cronies. It seems that when they're all together they all become

Hercules on their own. They think they've turned into Mighty Mouse, but he'd just turned into a very small mouse indeed. I jumped out the motor to confront him. Before I had a chance to say anything he told me he had nothing to do with what happened last night. Yeah, right? How did he know about last night, I thought, unless he'd just become a medium before the night was out. "That's good" I replied, "cause if you're not involved where are the people that were then?"

He was saved. All of a sudden it all came out, everything, more than enough. I was just glad people like that weren't on my side of the firm, cause he told all, which meant he knew nothing about a code of practice between him and his fellow cronies and definitely not the code of silence. He said where Mr. Ice was or where they might be. Wonder what he would have told the police if he was captured?

I then let the mouse scurry away. He'd now turned into a sly fox, because he'd told all and led me to the den. I stopped outside Hap's and phoned him. I told him we were going to hunt the no good being Mr Ice and 'EDUCATE HIM IN THE WAYS OF THE FIRM'. I took it on my own head, and told him the place where we were to find him. So off we went to get some petrol, and not for the car. We were like greyhounds chasing the rabbit, but instead of the rabbit we were now after the new fox, which was now Mr Ice and we were hot on his trail . . .

We ended up outside some flats were Mighty Mouse had said we could find them. We pulled up and checked the area out, then reversed the car out of sight. We walked down and in to the flats. I found the door that the Mouse had told me about, and being the sort of fella I am, instead of kicking off the door, I knocked calmly on it. Unlike the Ice man who seemed not to have known where the knocker was on Happy's the night before. After I'd put my head to the door to see if I could hear what was going on inside, I knocked calmly on the door. That's the difference between a gangster and a gentleman, I guess. One knocks while the other one kicks off the door.

No answer. I knocked again. Same response. We left. On the way back we thought it best to hide the tools we'd brought with us especially for this piece of work before it came on top and the police turned up, otherwise we'd be in big trouble. So back to Happy's, where we stashed the tools. We then went to get some chips. As we were driving to the chip shop, who should drive past but Mr. Ice with only one crony.

That was it. We were off, back on the trail in hot pursuit. We followed them to the flats where we'd just been, unbeknown to them, staying just back from their motor. I plotted up where I'd reversed the car before and we watched them walk in. We got out slowly and followed their footsteps. I stopped suddenly, realising we had no tools. If he pulled some thing out on us, what then? So I ran back to the motor and in the boot was my lucky bat. Lucky, because it always seemed to come out in times when I needed it, it like right now which was lucky. That's why I called it lucky. Out it came and it was pushed down the back of my jeans hidden by my jacket.

I walked back calmly to Happy and then back to the flat door. I stood to one side out of sight, ready for when the door came open. I pulled the bat out and was in the base ball pose ready for a home run when Happy knocked on the door. When the door opened, as I swung I managed to stop my self just in time before it made contact and gave me a home run. Thank God, because there in front of us was a woman. If the bat had hit her it would have taken her head clean out of the arena. I would have been so gutted if I had hit her, an innocent woman. All scared, she said"They're not here".

Well, sweetheart, we knew they were. I said "Sorry, sweetheart, can you do me a big favour?

She said "What?"

"Tell them I'm looking for them. They seemed to have left this in my car." As I pointed to the bat, saying I wanted to return it to them, she smiled nervously and shut the door. I lent against the door and heard her say that I was looking for them. It went dead.

Then I heard her say "Why do you keep bringing trouble to my door?" I couldn't hear any more. After that nothing happened and we left. The bat was replaced in its dwellings ready for its next lucky guest appearance.

After that Me and Happy went on as if nothing had happened. The threats stopped and I didn't see or hear any more of Mr. Ice for a while. I continued to work in the manor with no more dramas. I did catch up with Mr. Ice in prison. Like I said people turn up in the most unusual places and in places you wouldn't expect to see them. He turned up in prison where I was on a charge for cannabis which you'll hear about later, but by then Mr Ice had turned himself right around. H'ed become Mr. Nice and was most apologetic for the liberty he'd taken back then with my uncle and me. He said he was a proper mess back then and gave me his word it would never happen again. Whilst we were doing our porridge he helped me out a great deal with the canteen and a few other bits.

That's where it seems to count. You're sharing a cold, damp cell when all you have is your own thoughts to keep you company and a few photos and telephone calls. You also share some heart to hearts. You build up a sort of mutual respect and friendship for each other. Before long I found myself minding the cell door whilst the evil trade continued even in prison. My new role in there was looking out for Mr. Mage who was also from the Wood. You looked out for your own. Well, I did while I was in there, and I'd be enforcing long overdue canteen and tobacco debts that had been lent out and make sure it would all be paid back in double or as arranged. Also I only let one person in at a time in to the cells, to get what they needed. While the using and dealing went on, I'd watch the door for the screws.

The devil's powder still managed to find me, even in prison. Even from the depths of hell, as prison is for some people, I was still managing to sniff drugs. Crazy, I know. It seemed I couldn't stop myself even in there. Some things will never change, I thought. After I came out, I only lasted three days until the devil and his dandruff was all in my head again.

We met up after prison, the Iceman and me, and things seemed OK between us. We even did a bit of work here and there. So it was time to let sleeping dogs lie before one of us got seriously hurt, so I put the past to rest.

After that there were no problems in the manor. Things seemed to move on like clockwork and the selling continued.

A BIT OF PAINTING WORK...

Until I went out on a bit of work for a few old acquaintances of mine...

Before long I found myself being a get away driver. Of all the things I'd dreamed of being back then on the hill in Organ Hall, I was now sitting in a car ready for my accomplices. Well, I needed to earn some extra money to try to get some of the tick sorted I owed, and keep me all above board with Mr. B and the chimps.

But things don't always work out the way we'd like them. My self-respect was sliding by doing these mad little jobs here and there, but I needed a way to try and get above board with the money I owed or at least break even, cos I was sniffing more drugs than selling at times. So I needed other ways to get money, to try get me out this circus I'd created for myself, to keep my head above water, and keep the powder coming my way and Mr. B's chimps a long, long way behind me.

The more I sniffed, the more I had to sell, and the merry-go-round would go round and round like that. I even managed to sniff £10,000 from the bank and was leasing out my motors to other villains on hire purchase, to try and stay ahead with the cocaine debts I found myself with. It was time to look for other earners that might help out without hurting anyone.

Well, they'd just put the paintings in the back of my car when the alarm went off and the lights went on in the shop.

I hated it when that happened. We were out of there, on to the A1 coming back from the scene of the crime, when I looked in the mirror and saw the police. In no time at all we were pulled to the hard shoulder and the boys in blue were all over the car like a rash. They searched the car and had me out and told me to open the boot. (Luckily, this time there were no dead bodies in it).

Anyhow, the policeman had clocked the paintings. "Hello, hello! What do we have here then, hey?"

"Well, officer, my dad's moving house and he told me to keep them in there cos there was no room in the van, and I said I'd bring them back to the new house in the morning."

"Ok, son."

What,I thought. He believed me? Well, I nearly believed it my self too. He handed me the producer and told me to be on my way. Nice man. It had come on top but we were away with the paintings and the police might have been kicking themselves when they realised we now needed a place to hide them. They were getting very hot. So much so they'd have burnt your hands if you'd picked them up. Being me, I knew just the place to hide them. My accomplices agreed they could only trust me so I dropped everyone off and went to hide the hot goods.

I remembered that a little while ago I'd met some nice people. In this game you get to socialise and meet with all sorts of people from all walks of life. Some are nice and some are not so nice. Some are rich, some are poor, some are famous and some have never been heard of.

These people had become good friends of mine. They were running a radio station on an estate we'll call Graham Park. I'd go there sometimes and give shouts to other pals in London and promote tickets for raves like the one I called the Three Aces. Their names... well, we'll call them Steven and Mandy. They had a nice place the last time I was round there. I'd met them through other friends, and they told me once while I was around there having dinner (and some after dinner sniff, as we'd run out of mints) that if I ever needed a place to stay or I ever needed to leave anything of mine there, I could.

No problems. They went out of their way to make me feel as comfortable and welcome as possible. It was nice to have a place to have a rest from all the madness in my own manor.

It was getting late. It must have been about 1 o'clock. As Steve opened the door and said "Come in", he looked in a right state. I followed him in to the front room. Wow! What had happened to my friends, I thought. When I'd been there seven months ago the house had been nice. They'd had loads of home comforts. Now all they had was a little portable T.V on a little table and the settee. A small photo of the nice looking Mandy was on top of the T.V. I sat down on the settee and asked where Mandy was. Steve said in a sad voice that she was at work. When I asked when she'd be home, he told me he didn't know. She worked all sort of hours. This seemed was a bit disturbing to me, as it was about 12.45 p.m. or thereabouts.

Then Steve said to excuse him as he'd started to inject his arm. This was too much for me. I had to look away. My friends, what had happened to them, I thought. The drugs had clearly messed them up, as they do. Well, after his hit I said "Steve, what's happened?" He said that he'd been working with a firm and started to sell heroin, something I never got myself in to. There's a line and that was it for me, or I just hadn't crossed it yet or never intended to. He also told me that his pretty kind little Mandy was now working the streets. She had become a prostitute. How could this have happened?

He continued to say they'd both started to use the drug instead of selling it and that the only way they now could afford to pay it off was to sell their stuff from the house and for Mandy to go out and do what she was doing. I stopped him dead and changed the subject to save him his embarrassment. "Steve, I need to stay the night and need to be up really early for the morning. So could I stay?"

He said it was cool and grabbed an alarm clock and showed me to one of the bedrooms. It was bare, only carpet and wall paper. "Will that be OK?"

I said "Steve, its fine mate". On the floor were some pillows, a sheet and a quilt, no bed, so I made one up on the floor. I was getting used to sleeping rough. It was better than sleeping in the car as I'd done some nights when others went to bed that I'd been out partying with, not because I had nowhere to go, just because I'd get in to a state with the cocaine I was using or would be buzzing night and day and didn't want the party to end, even if they had. I found it hard to sleep, so I'd find myself crashing at other pals' or women's houses instead of going home.

Mum hadn't come from this era and to see her son messed up like this must have been hard. She wasn't part of the drug culture either, and was definitely far from the rave scene. I often wondered what mum and dad would think if they'd a proper inkling of what I was really up to. I must have put mum and dad through so much heartache back then, but they still went out their way to do their very best for me.

I put the alarm clock to the side ready for it to go off in the morning, put my head on the pillow and a thousand thoughts entered through my head about how messed up life really was. Now I knew that Mandy had started to do that, surely there was a another way. How had I created this circus around me? I was now also in thoughts of how I might get out of it, which amounted to nothing, just to get nicked and that was a long way off the cards back then. I still had a few more aces to play before the inevitable happened.

Before long it was 1.30 a.m. and I'd drifted off to sleep.

THE UNINVITED YARDIE BROTHERS...

BANG! Off came the door like a bomb had gone off. In came the Yardies. I woke up with the noise. My heart shuddered for a moment. From then on everything moved on in slow motion. I heard people shouting "Stay where you are blood clart and don't move man!" I glanced at the clock. 3.3O a.m. Shit! Surely Steve wasn't being raided at this time? Not now, not with me there and not with the paintings going missing.

I hadn't noticed any strange motors, vans or even motorbikes the police used to plot up in and observe the sights. Or any twitching curtains where Old Bill would be happily taking photos from neighbours' houses. Ready for the big day when it clearly was a bust for them and a trip to jail for us. And I knew my motor wasn't bugged just yet, which they do some times without you knowing when they have an investigation out on you or have you under observation. They need to gather all the correct info to seal the case to send it to the C.P.S before it goes to convince a judge for a warrant for a bust.

Like when I got nicked for the cannabis they were plotted up in the neighbour's house. They could have warned me to stop or told me the police were there. After all we spoke nearly every day. Well, I was told after that they were there. Too late by then. I guess money and a clean street meant more to them but rightly so. It was neighbourhood watch and they were watching.

Then I heard loud Jamaican voices. Next thing in came a Yardie brother. The light hit my eyes from outside, and all I could see was a stocky looking figure. As my eyes started to adjust I saw he was pointing some thing at me. My eyes focused fully on what it was he was holding: a shooter at my chest, and a large one at that. Now he was pushing me down on to the bedding and then he told me to get up and move in to the front room. Well, it's hard to argue when someone's finger's on the trigger of a sawn-off shoot gun. I guess I wasn't waking up to breakfast or looking at the paper, more like looking down the barrel of a gun.

The Yardie told me to get dressed and to lie down on the front room floor. As I was on the floor I noticed there were four of the brothers, one holding a gun to Steve's head, another by the door, one with his knee in the small of my back, and one standing by the window, sort of keeping watch. I was stretching my eyes up to try and see Steve more and what was going on, whilst sweating, I might add. Well, they were screaming at Steve for their payments and by the sound of it they were long overdue. Then after what seemed like ages who should turn up but little Mandy? The poor girl, after all the abuse she'd put herself through all night with different punters, then coming home to this! My heart went out to her.

The brother by the door grabbed her by the hair and dragged her in to the front room. He ripped her bag from her arm. Out fell make-up and other unimportant stuff, then a load of money. The brother bent down, picked it up and screamed "What's this! That's not enough!" Well, my guess was there must have been around £800 there so how much did they owe? Far more I guess than what they had there, since the brother turned to Steve and said, "This is no good, pussy clart. Where's the rest?"

Steve begged, "Please, please, five more days! It'll be all paid."

The brother lost the plot and screamed "Five more fucking days, man, five fucking days, man! You had that a week ago!" He paced the room, then slapped Steve with the side of the gun, which made him drop to the floor. The brother then turned to the Mandy and pulled her nearer to him and started to tear off her top and pushed her on to the settee revealing her naked breasts. I could see tears roll down her cheeks. My eyes closed and my brain engaged. Surely someone must have heard the door being kicked off? Well no one came to help if they had. Was this a dream? Would the alarm clock go off and I'd be getting ready to get rid of the paintings and changing my number plates back over on the car? But no, it was far from any dream. It was a proper nightmare, one that was happening right now. this was reality. I knew if they raped Mandy and shot one of us we were all dead. "Stop!" I said.

Shit, what had happened there? Well I guess when you're scared and put in a situation like this anything seems to come in to your mind then your mouth. Well "Stop!" had just come out of my mouth very unwillingly. They all turned to me and now the spotlight was on me with all their eyes staring at me with daggers pointing in my direction. It was there again, "Stop! I've got the rest of the dough", I yelled, knowing full well I didn't. I didn't have two bob which became my nickname after that because I never had any money because I was sniffing it all. With that I was pulled up from the floor and ushered through the door.

Saying I had their dough seemed to have had the correct effect. After all they had left Mandy shaking on the settee half naked, covering herself with her arm across herself and Steve still lying there still, with blood coming from his wounds.

Before long I was pushed into a Mercedes minding my head as the Old Bill do when they push you in their motors. Now I had two medium sized brothers on either side of me in the back with their gun resting on their laps pointed at me. The driver put his large gun into the boot. It was a sawn off. Then the driver got in and turned round and grunted at me "Where to, pussy clart?"

I said nervously "To B/WOOD".

He kissed his teeth "Chah, man, I know it well" and then off we went for what seemed the longest drive in silence until we arrived outside the garage of mine. (This is a lesson I learnt well from that day on. Never bring gangsters to your home, especially not gun men and people looking for money that you definitely didn't have and more so, not in the middle of the night"). One brother let me out and lent on the roof of the Merc staring at me whilst I opened the garage. I could have run but what good was that? They were at my house. So I just looked into the garage. Looking round frantically I saw a piece of metal pipe, which was no good. They had a gun. What was I going to do? I then saw tins of paint. I looked back very nervously. The brother shouted "Come on!" as I walked into the garage a bit further. I just got a glimpse of a briefcase under some paper work. It was dusty so I blew the dust off and ran back to the car. I was in big trouble now. After all I didn't even know what was in the briefcase. Well, as luck would have it I was back in the car without them wanting to look in the briefcase just yet, resting the briefcase on my knees.

The brother got in and off we went. The driver said "London" so London it was. I had escaped them wanting to look in the case which was well lucky but now I was on my way to London! They seemed to be in a bit of a hurry. What for I didn't know or want to ask. I'd never been in a Merc before, as I thought to try to get my mind off what was really going to happen. We arrived at some big tower block flats and all got out. The guns were concealed in their trench jackets and it was as if I was being minded towards the flats with all four of them around me and by my side. At the bottom we were greeted by another brother who had a walkie-talkie. He looked up at the flats and radioed up, so we then went up but the other brother stayed down where he was.

As we got to the door where we were to go in, another brother was waiting, watching us. The driver of the car banged on the door. The first door was opened. Then the brother looked through the metal enforcement that secured the main door. After the gate and the main door had been opened they smiled at each other and in we went. We could see into the front room. There was reggae playing softly, more brothers drinking, and women who were all dressed in short dresses and had suspenders all on show. They looked like they were working girls. They were smoking rocks. That was the last I saw as I was pushed into one of the bedrooms.

But the others that were minding me didn't follow in after me. They were greeted loudly by the people who were already there, sitting behind a big table with loads of money, drugs and loads of neatly stacked bundles of money with elastic bands wrapped around them and drug paraphernalia and a gun. There was a big muscle dread wearing a string vest and next to him a smaller version of himself, with no vest but loads of gold chains round his neck. A smaller brother was looking out the window with binoculars and talking to people to come up on the radio. So now it was crunch time. I was in London with the brothers, with no money, which they obviously wanted by the trouble they'd gone through at Steve's and to bring me there. And all I had was this briefcase. It dawned on me no one knew where I was, and that they might be getting rid of me by throwing me out with the rubbish.

The big dread stood up and looked at the briefcase, so I handed it to him. He let out a large amount of smoke from the joint he was smoking into my face and smiled, flashing a gold tooth. He pulled his dreads together and tied them back with a elastic band, cleared a space on the table, put the case down, spun it round, rubbed his hands together then flipped the catch to pop the case open. The dread with the gold chains leaned forward and his eyes went wide.

Now my legs had turned to jelly. My body was cold but sweat was dripping off me. In so many words my arse hole had well and truly fallen out. It's not every day you get stuck in the middle of the night in the loins den in this sort of position that I'd now found myself in. My life now had turned into a proper circus and I'd created it. It was getting worse by the minute as now I was about to be a clown.

Things were getting much worse now the dread had seen into the case. He stood up and launched the case at the wall, which made me jump. As the bits fell on to the floor all around us. my heart skipped a beat. Of course there wasn't any money in there. That only happens in the movies. There was just some moody calculator and some pens and other little bits and bobs, which were far from being valuable. He grabbed the gun from the table and rushed forward to me. Now this was the sort of nightmare where you know you should run but your feet don't work. He pushed the shooter into my mouth. The front of my teeth chipped and I felt the coldness of the metal on my tongue. The chips are still there to this day. He screamed, "Why have you come here without my money, man?" his blood shot eyes staring into mine.

I wanted to say "Well, to be honest I didn't want to come here", but he didn't want to hear that and even if I could have said it, I'm sure I couldn't cos it's hard to talk with your mouth full up and even harder with a shooter pushed in it.

He pulled the shooter from my mouth and said "Well?"

Shaking like a leaf I said that I'd work the money off.

He rested the gun on my head. Bang! The gun went off. My head went dizzy, my legs buckled and I hit the floor with a thud. I felt wet all in the front of my pants. Next thing I had a woman slapping my face. I must have gone to heaven or was this just a joke hell plays on you before you enter? That's painful thinking. You've got a nice bird to greet you and guide you through the gate before she pushes you in to the fire and turns in to the devil.

I came to. I had collapsed with fright and, yes, pissed my pants. Well, you may laugh, but what would you have done? (Thought so, you'd have stayed back at Steve's. Well, I wouldn't blame you if you had). I thought what don't kill you must make you that bit stronger but I was far from feeling strong at that moment. The dread was laughing with his pal. I looked behind me and there were bullet holes in the wall just above where my head was. He had done it to scare me and it had worked. I was scared the woman who was now leaning over me wasn't amused and was very paranoid from the crack smoking and the noise of the gun. The woman had come in to see what all the drama was about and thought the same as I had, that the brother had put a hole in me.

The two dreads continued to laugh. Then the gunman said, not laughing, that I'd be working the money off and he had just the job for me to do and it was worth my life on it. So now I was told that I'd be picked up from where his boys had taken me to the garage in two weeks after he'd got my details ready for my job. I was then put into a cab because the driver of the Merc said there was no way I was sitting in his Merc now which was understandable. After all, who wants a man in your motor who's pissed his pants? Now I found myself being driven back in a cab, which they had nicely paid for considering I now owed them.

Before long I was back at Steve and Mandy's. They were pleased with me as you can imagine. I had left a Two Bob, and had arrived back in their eyes a hero. I left Steve and Mandy's biting my lip. I was mad inside but kept a brave face on. After all I was still alive and they weren't to know what would happen that night.

What a night! After changing my clothes it was now 9 a.m. I was well behind schedule. I needed to sort the plates back over on the car and get the paintings sold. I knew just the place to go to get rid of them.

As I was driving towards my friend, Windows, house it came to me that if I got copies of these paintings I could have another earner under my sleeve so I hand braked the car round and continued in the opposite direction driving through the smoke that had come up from the tyres heading to my pal who was well into printing money, which as you can imagine can come in pretty handy some times. Like with the rose sellers, the window wash man, the pizza man and just about any man that don't look at his money. (Normally it's in one hand and out the other). Well, for most of us it is. You wouldn't be looking at each note to see that the Queen was winking back at you as it was on his notes. They seemed to work even though it was proper Mickey Mouse money.

I showed my pal the paintings; he knew the crack straight away. "You want these copied just as if they were the real ones?"

"No, I want to stick them on your wall!" Of course I wanted them copied! It didn't take a rocket scientist to work it out, did it? Well, after what seemed like most of the day and half the night, the copied paintings were nearly done. They looked the part so much it was hard to tell the real ones from the snide so we bagged them ready to be sold to a French fella who could shift them in France. Well, I guess it beats selling onions. It was right up the French fella's street when we told him we had the real ones for him, well near enough real. I told my printing pal to keep the money that I'd make from these copies safe for a rainy day which hasn't come yet and I'd forgoten about it until now. So don't worry I'll soon be collecting it in. I even took a couple of prints myself; they looked blinding hanging up in my gaff. I then took the originals to Windows.

WINDOWS...

Window's place was always open, morning, noon and night, at the weekends and sometimes in the week. It seemed to be a haven for the no good, the dodgy plus the strange. Some of the best blaggers and speechers far more experienced than the pub ones would be there. These ones were pros. For them it was a means of survival. Some were young, some were old and a few looked liked they had escaped from the London dungeons. Some right shady characters would turn up and not forgetting a few Irish travelling chavs, prostitutes and the homeless. On the odd occasion I got to know a few of them well. There would be the odd women there too. You had to keep your eyes well open and you couldn't leave anything lying around, as it would mysteriously go missing. Then knowing full well they had taken it the girls would turn round with puppy dog eyes and say "I don't know where it could be". (Well it was in their pocket ready to be sold as soon as you left). These people would be there to haggle or barter with goods and bits and bobs they'd got or that were hot and needed to be got rid of. They wouldn't receive anywhere near the value for them and some would be happy with some drugs here and there. So it was a deal for a steal, a steal because it was nearly being stolen from them. They were being robbed and not even by wearing a mask. (It was day light robbery for them). They went away happy so things were all good.

The place belonged to Mr. Salubrious. He was like the Pied Piper, because all the street rats would come to him and treat his gaff like a youth hostel. The place was like an Aladdin's cave, full with goods of all sorts. Mr. Salubrious came across as a nice fella or he tried his best to be. To certain people he was a reasonable man and always seemed reasonable to me whenever we met. He'd often done the odd favour for me like picking me up and driving me around so it was harder for the police to keep up with you. He was a man who took everything in his stride. Whenever I'd arrive he'd be in the middle of catching his z and doing his trade. He had a sidekick who was like Neanderthal man, as he was still living in the prehistoric age where he thought it was still right to slap women around, like he took the liberty of doing once. Some people seem to have no respect. I arrived and he was in bed with two women. Now this was normal thing. The women were dressed on top much to his disappointment and he was undressed in the bed with a woman on either side. They were his helpers or you could say his bitches. He could have passed for King Jaffey Gofer the way he looked or King of the Speed Heads.

He was definitely in denial. The drugs had corrupted his mind and he couldn't see it as it's hard to when drugs are going round in your head most days. His poison was speed, which had put his appearance into a shady existence of his former self. I would often go round there with gifts of the smoke ball stuff and share his company with a little devil's dandruff and collect some money and just chat. At times it was pleasant and it always seemed after my rounds at the end of a night and when he'd put his guitar down. I'm sure he thought he was the darkness when he'd gone off on one of his speed and guitar frenzies, but he was talented in his own right.

It was nice to see him on occasions and see the different characters turn up; some were entertaining at times and would bring a smile or laughter to my face. He woke up, and I showed him the paintings. He said they were Salubrious' paintings so I told him the price, not what I had in mind but it was a take it or leave it position I found myself in, and the offer wasn't that bad. Nothing to write home about as they still had their prices tags on the side of them. So in other words it was sale of the century as they were well hot. He said they would bring warmth to someone's home and I'm sure he was right.

Now they were sold it was back to meet my panting thieves to share the dough out. The money was shared out and it all went on more devil's dandruff and a few escort birds, which seemed a normal thing back then. When really it should have gone towards getting me out of the circus, but it seemed it wasn't time to get out just yet. I guess I couldn't see myself getting out on my own, even if I tried, the devil's dandruff had a strong hold on me, as it has so many people. I was still playing the clown but I wasn't laughing inside. It was killing me. So with the paintings gone, money squandered and the women seen to, it seemed I was stuck in the middle of this circus with no way out and pretending to be Charley Large Potatoes.

I'd always ask the escort girls why they did what they did. It baffled me why such nice looking women would want to put themselves through what they had, or any woman. Being a man it confused me the stuff you think about when you've got a head full of the devil's dandruff. I guess that's why I called it that. They would all try to justify it and tell me the same story. It's like they all sat down together and learned what to say if ever asked. I guess money meant more to them too and the sex was good some times. At least they got to try out most if not all of their fantasies. Sometimes it could be dangerous for them too. After all, you never know what sort of punter you're going to get. You never know who's out there. Maybe they couldn't see a way out also.

There's got to be more to life than money, I'd think, lying in my bed messed up from the cocaine welling round my brain like a tornado while every one was helping themselves to my cocaine and the women to the thing in my pants. Not being able to sleep or get my thought on one topic without it dithering off on to another before I had time to finish studying all the avenues of the first. What about the priceless finer things in life? Surely money just can't keep you happy? There was more to it. There had to be even for them.

I met some nice working women. It seems that working women and drug dealers seem to attract each other. Don't know why. It just happens that way. Some became just good company (as in going out with them) and some became friends. They would phone and we would go out when I was messed up which was nearly every day back then. Why they spent their hard earned money on me, I don't know. They all seemed to have this messed up attitude for some reason. Maybe it was because of what they were putting themselves through. It must play with their emotions and mess up their minds. They must be very lucky if they do find some one who does really care about them and tries to forget their past (if they knew about it) and loves them for who they are, not what they were. Not a lot of men can accept a past like that. I guess it could be a lonely world being on your own with no true partner. Or maybe it wasn't my business to ask that sort of question or give my opinion.

It seemed everywhere I looked people just wanted material things and I was one of them. I didn't want to be working all the hours like mum and dad for nothing but if I looked closer it weren't for nothing. Even though they were poor they still had a happy contented life, so they had more than most. I'd had enough already of the life I'd been leading. I'd been in this game long enough to know it came with a lot of bullshit, mistrust and slyness. Whether from acquaintances, working women or some pals, or your own women or women who just liked the game you were in, not you, just the powder and the little control it bought with it.

I wasn't one to get excited about things until they happened. I'd heard too many promises from people who were just fly-by-night talkers. Talk was cheap, as I'd found out by asking them sort of women and trusting the wrong sort of people. With cocaine you're forever trying to be nice and charming and it takes a lot of enjoyment and energy out of you. Using like I was I didn't want to be around people or talk to them. How could you with these people? You learned not to trust anybody, even people who were close. You were still sceptical, whether it was working birds blagging you or acquaintances, or people you thought were pals. You didn't stand a chance in this circus. That's why you couldn't turn to no one when you did have problems or needed help or comforting. In this game the world could be a lonely cold place even if you had a lot going for you.

The two weeks passed by and before I knew it, it was time for me to do this job for the Yardie brothers with me not knowing what they'd planned for me. They arrived at my garage again, the two brothers, the ones that were in the Merc that night but only the driver and his pal. Not all four heavies, only two this time. I was told to pack a bag with a few clothes, not knowing where I was heading. They said I was going on a little trip and I'd best get my passport. I was a bit worried but I had to go. Before long I was taken to the airport. I didn't think I'd be paying my debt off in another country.

A TRIP TO JAMAICA...

We boarded a plane and were heading for Jamaica. On the plane I asked what the job was and they said not to worry just yet and that I'd find out in a few days. I should enjoy myself while I could, while I was out in Jamaica with them. (If this is how they treated people that owed them money then I should have asked for a bit more, hey?) They seemed to be OK and weren't as aggressive as the other night. We talked to each other on the plane as if we'd known each other for years. It was a lot better than shouting at me and pushing a shooter to my head. We even started to have a laugh.

We landed in Jamaica after a long but enjoyable flight. As I stepped out of the plane and started to walk down the steps, the warm heat just hit me. What a place!

Sandy beaches and tall trees with coconuts and bananas hanging from them, the sun beating down on the Caribbean Sea and lapping at the golden sands. The friendly people just going about their business and taking things in their stride. Reggae music was playing from the cars and busses passing by. Taxi men were playing dominoes at the side of the road. I saw all this driving from the airport with the two brothers to a shanty town where we were to stay not far from the beach.

That's where we stayed for most of the week, sitting on the beach tripping out from smoking weed, drinking rum out of coconuts, watching women and just relaxing. letting time just pass by. We also ate salt fish, ackee and dumplings. I sat on the beach one night just watching the sea lap at the shore watching the stars in the sky. They looked like diamonds on a dark blue carpet. Was this all life was about, trying to always chase a pound note? It seemed the notes I was chasing would always end up in my nose, or someone else's pocket. Then it came to me that no one knew I was in Jamaica.

Well, three days passed and on the third day we all went out on a blue and white speedboat, which must have belonged to the driver of the Merc. The brothers had met up with some women and brought them with us. They were very nice! (Not one to boast, but let's have it right, if they were nice you'd make a point of telling people, hey?) We were all on the speed boat gliding through the sea like a hot knife cutting butter, with the sun beating its hot rays down on us. The three women were lying in the back in small bikinis and being cooled off as the surf was splashing up and hitting us and the warm hot wind was shooting past. They were eating fruit and sharing it with us.

The driver of the Merc was now the driver of the speedboat. He really opened up the engine and the boat jumped forward further in to the sea. I was sitting on the front of the boat when one of the women came over to me, now topless, and asked if I could cream her up. Well, I nearly fell off the boat. Of course I could! So I stood up and noticed that the other two girls were with the other brothers. So here I was in the middle of nowhere creaming up a Caribbean beauty who was now sitting in between my legs letting me rub her sexy body down with sun cream.

As I finished rubbing sun cream all over her she stood up and slid out of her bottoms. I couldn't believe my mince pies as she jumped down the step and walked to the back of the boat and lay down on her front again. As she jumped her nicely shaped curved bum and firm breasts gave a little bounce and a wiggle. Wow, this was the life! I could get used to this, I thought. I did feel a little bit out of place being the only white fella and not knowing anyone too well. That didn't stop them treating me well and when the cocaine came out we could have been best of friends after a few lines and opening some champs. We were all sharing in death talks and having a laugh.

Well, time was moving on and before long we'd stopped out in the middle of the sea when a yacht came out to meet us. It pulled up at the side of our boat and the driver of the yacht came aboard. He handed a large parcel in a bag to our driver. Then he said "Hi" and had a few lines himself and a few sips of the champs. Afterwards he climbed back on to his yacht and sped off into the sunshine as if he'd never been there at all.

When we got back the women disappeared. This hit me like an avalanche. I was driven to a place with the parcel from the yacht. The fun stopped as quickly as it had started. It was crunch time. I was strapped up with the parcel and told we were going home early. The only thing now was I was coming home with this parcel stuck to me. So this was the job the dread had in mind that was worth my life! I couldn't do this, but I had to. I had no choice. No one knowing where I was or knowing what had happened that night when I was in the flat in London, when this had been forced upon me. Not even Steve and Mandy knew. They thought I'd sorted things out and paid off their debts.

I was in Jamaica strapped up with whatever, not knowing because it was not visible and we were leaving today in about five minutes. We were driven back to the airport. Now, as you can imagine, I felt sick. I couldn't do this. Was I coming home at all? I began to shake. I said "Listen" desperately. "I can't do this".

With that the two brothers turned back to how they were that first night. "We know where you live and if you don't do this or pay us, one of your families can." As they entered my ears the words felt like they were cutting into me like a knife. Well, that was enough to get me into the airport. After all, this had nothing to do with my family. This was my own circus or you could say shit I was in.

Now the brothers stayed just behind me enough to look like they were travelling by themselves. What chance did I have, a white fella, suntanned with a red Adidas hat on, in just my shorts and top, leaving Jamaica with extra luggage, this parcel? I walked sweating to the check point, took a deep breath and handed the passport to the guard. He looked down and handed it back. I walked slowly though the checkpoint feeling very uneasy. The thought crossed my mind, what if I died or never saw my family again? Worse still, what if one of my family got it? Or I ended up with a ten stretch? I hadn't a great deal of choice.

As I walked out on to the airfield ready to board the plane the brothers said "See, it isn't that bad, hey? Well, not for them it weren't but looking in my pants they would have seen just how bad it was for me. I'd even prayed on the way through. I was still scared on the plane. So much so I don't even want to talk to them or any one. We took off but I was far from feeling comfortable or relaxed. To my amazement I'd got through. In my head was a big void.

When the plane was landing I felt much worse than before. I felt like the fella on the Midnight Express. If I got caught would they believe me? Was it was still a trip to jail or a trip to the graveyard if I mentioned the truth? That's when a story can sometimes come in handy in a crisis like this. Again I tried. "I can't do this"

The brother's reply was "Listen man. I know. I know. I understand".

So it was do or die, or get ten years. I walked up to the customs desk. The officer looked at me. "Passport, please". My heart was beating so hard I'm sure he could have heard it above all the other noise that was going on in the airport. "Can I check your bag, sir?"

"OK." I handed him my bag. He then slid it through the machine and handed me the passport back. "Have a nice day sir".

"Yes" I mumbled, wanting to be out of there and in safety away from the brothers and from getting a ten stretch. As I walked through the detector. "Bing" Off it went. No! Yes, it had gone off. Every thing moved in slow motion after that. Noises started to echo, my mouth went dry, and my hands started to ache. I felt dizzy and my eyes were blurred. The room spun and round the guard looked at where the parcel was concealed. No. Now this was a don't pass go, don't collect two hundred pounds and move directly to jail position I had just found myself in. It was over, finished.

"Your belt, sir".

All surprised I said "Oh". I guess if we were playing Monopoly the Community Chest had just turned over and given me a much-needed get out of jail free card. I took off my belt and put it on the side nervously. I walked through and picked up my bag. As I was about to walk away the guard at the other end stopped me, just as the two brothers were handing their passports to the other guard I'd just passed. "You've left your belt sir." I walked back, picked it up and as I walked past the guard on the other side he said, "Don't worry, son. That happens all the time". Well, I guess it does. People getting mixed up with the wrong people at the wrong time and finding themselves in a desperate situation where they're risking their life. You read about it in the papers all the time. The guard wasn't wrong. If only he'd known what I was doing, I'm sure he wouldn't have been so helpful and polite. I said goodbye, then walked quickly away towards the outside of the airport, past the armed police, out to where we were to get a taxi from. All the time the brothers were not far behind me, watching my every move. What a nightmare!

That was one of the worst experiences I had been through in my life. Much worse than the time when I had twenty five stitches put into my face when I was looking out for a old acquaintance of mine and looking out for a few girls over in Stanbrough Lakes. A fight broke out with two travellers, and whilst fighting with one of them the other one took a vodka bottle out of his bag and thought he would even things up a bit by smashing it across my nut. This didn't stop me making a mess of the one I had on the floor, and was giving a left and right too until the other one pushed the broken bit in to my mouth whilst saving his pal who managed to get up and do a runner. The other one saw my face and dropped the broken bottle and ran himself. It was a hi-de-hi-de-hoh and off we go. This all happened while my acquaintance did a runner too and left me to sort his mess out for him. I had done a good job of one but the other one left me to pick the rest of my face up from where the bottle went in it. (The things we do for pals).

We left the airport in a taxi. I'd made it through. We were now driven to London. We arrived and the parcel was cut free from me. It felt like kryptonite did to Superman. Once it was off and out of my hands my normal senses came back and the scared ones took a little back seat. The brothers left the room with it and left me sitting on the seat just sitting there thinking what would happen to me next. In what seemed like only seconds the big dread, the one that had put the gun to my head that night, came in with a big smile on his face. He said "Well done, man". He pushed his fist together and told me to "Touch, man" so I did. He then said "This is for your troubles" and handed me more cocaine, about an ounce in one lump with a little bit of loose powder round it. I couldn't get away from the stuff! If I tried the devil was in my head and his dandruff was up my nose. I thanked the dread and he said, "You have bollocks man to do that and to risk everything for your no good friends", meaning Steve and Mandy.

I asked if every thing was OK between us now and them and he said "Safe, man. They're not getting any more of me." Then he continued with if I ever wanted to come and work for him or link up for more cocaine then he was the man. He said he knew loads of firms all over and he said he had his hands in most pies and he knew loads of dangerous people in this country and others in other countries. He handed me a number I could contact him on, then in came the other brothers that I'd gone to Jamaica with. They got out a few lines for us all. Then one of them said "Come bredrin. Let's get you back home."

Before long I was outside my house getting out the Merc. "Take care, man. Respect, man. It was good to meet you, Ginger." It seemed doing what I'd done had earned me some sort of little respect but at great cost, I thought. Something I wouldn't be doing again. Well, until I went to Ibiza. Now I was home and inside I pulled out the cocaine that had been given to me. I smashed some of the big lump and started to sniff line after line after line as it shattered all over the glass table. It seemed that one line was never enough and a thousand was too many. Within eight hours I had done the lot or near enough. I lay on my bed. My heart was beating heavily, my head was way off in the clouds. I was sweating and shaking and feeling paranoid and a bit horny too. I thought of what I'd done. I had sniffed the lot of the devil's dandruff and not got a penny back of it to pay off Mr. B. for the tickers I'd had. I finally managed to get off to sleep after the madness buzzing around my head. It was all over and time to move on from all that.

SANDRA AND THE TOM FOOLERY (JEWELLERY)...

Time moved on and I was still in the circus. I was creating and still chasing the debts and working for Mr. B. I had met up with a woman we'll call Stella. She of course liked the odd sniff here and there as I found out a bit later on. It was arranged that I was to meet a Liverpool firm member in London and collect £38,000 in cash from him. Also to pick up a motor and drive it to Knightsbridge. We met up in a nice restaurant in Selfridges in Oxford Street. A very posh restaurant indeed. It was well out of my league, me being a two bob as I'd sniff all the dough I'd ever made. I'd never seen the likes of these places. Well seen them, but not been in them. It was a far cry from the Chinese, Indian or MacDonald's that I was used to.

I didn't look out of place there because the firm had also gone out their way to buy me an Armani suit to wear for this special occasion, which was nice of them. I had to wear it anyway as that was the arrangement. I would have looked well out of place walking in there to collect this dough in a pair of jeans and a shirt. But suited and booted was how the firm wanted me so that's how I went. No questions asked. When I did have questions they would say. **"What are you, Old Bill or some thing? What we tell you is all you need to know for the job. Nothing more and nothing less. OK, son?"** That way if it did come on top. That's all I knew, and I'd be briefed with what to say if I was caught. Which was say nothing, till their doggy lawyer had sorted out the best story for me or found a loophole in the case or been given a few quid in back handers to get me off. I didn't know much so couldn't give much away. Not that I would, of course. I liked it that way. No one could blame me then if something did come out. It was hard to turn jobs down, as when you owed money that was the only way to lose bits of debts you owed. If you owed money they had control of you and your life. If you play a dangerous game you play it by dangerous rules. The rules are you must pay otherwise you get hurt, or end up dead in a little accident or in the Thames with concrete boots on. And with the connection they had the Old Bill would close the case with another gang killing or accident or make it look like it was a suicide. It was best to do these jobs as if I 'd been given more devil's dandruff to sell I'd probably have sniffed most of it and just paid back what was given and none of the debt.

The Liverpool firm's fella was already in the restaurant. I came to the door and rang the mobile number the firm had given me for him. "Hello, mate" he answered in a Scouse accent.

"Where are ya?"

"Calm down, calm down. I'm here. Table just behind the door. Turn round now. You'll see me". He must have been in about his late thirties or early forties; he was with a big chimp. Now this fella must have been at least twenty two stone and a body builder but bigger than most. It looked like he had to be greased to be squeezed into his suit, he was so large. For all I know he could have been deaf and dumb as he never really talked, just looked menacing. I guess that's what he was paid to do and he did his job well.

The reception fella took me over to the table where I was to sit down. "Hello mate." I put my hand to shake the big lump's hand and it nearly covered my whole arm. His hands were like shovels. He shook my hand and just glared at me.

He said "It's all there."

I thought he hadn't anything to give me but I told him "Thanks very much".

"There's some more money in two months on your firm's next drop". He ordered some thing to eat and asked what I wanted. I gave him a little studying glance as our food arrived. We ate in silence then his phone went off. He walked out the restaurant but soon returned. "Got to go now, lad. Something's come up and I need to get on". With that he leant forward and said "The dough's in the motor outside" as he pushed the keys to me under a napkin. Then he whipped out a wedge of dough and slung about £150 on the table. I finished off the grub and looked at the £150. It was much more than the bill. The fella must have been caker boo to throw money around like that. I ordered dessert from the waiter and picked up the keys from under the napkin and the rest of the money and walked outside to see where the motor was and to check on the dough. I came out on to the high street just out side the restaurant. I looked around for a motor until I saw a little blue Ford Fiesta. That must be it, I thought as I made my way towards it.

I pushed the alarm box when the lights on a brand new red Japanese motor flashed on and off as the locks clicked in one synchronised movement. Surely not? This motor was a serious bit of kit. It was a sports car with two doors and two seats and the lights popped out of the bonnet. The alloys were gleaming so much it looked like it had just fallen of a car transporter on its way to the mainland. It was green, with leather in side, and with a computer on board. The only bad thing was, it spoke in Japanese. It had a TV in the roof that came down when parked and the roof buttons were pressed. When I was pressing them, I thought they were for the sun roof!

I was in love. The car must have been worth about £45,000. The dashboard talked to you but I couldn't understand it so I just watched the little pictures to work out what it was saying. The sound system was proper nice. When I turned it on the soft crisp sound of Luther Vandross came out. This car was the don! It was fully loaded with all the extras. You name it, it had it.

I walked carefully over to it trying to conceal my excitement. Because motors like this were new to me, I was expecting some moody motor to drive back in. I slowly opened the door. There on the floor was a briefcase. I shut the door behind me, pulled the case up on to my lap and went to unclip it. When I looked down it was a combination lock. Now how did I know the dough was in there? Then I rang the number for the Scouser.

"Hello mate", he answered.

I replied "I'm in the motor and I can't open the case", "Calm down" he said. "The number's in the ashtray" "OK".

The phone went dead. I pulled the ashtray open. There it was: the piece of paper with the number on it. I flicked the numbers round as quickly as possible and was getting excited, when click, the clips opened. I slowly lifted up the case lid and paused, and then whistled. There it was: rows of £50 notes staring back at me. I nearly got a hard on. I phoned my firm "The painter has just dropped of the Queens portraits" I said.

"Ok you know what to do next". Nowadays you have to be so careful what you say on the phone with all this new High-Tec knowledge the police and MI5 and the other under cover agents they have. I shut the case, flicked the numbers round and hid it back under the passenger seat. I got out the motor, shut the door and pressed the alarm. Beep! The doors locked again. I walked back into the restaurant towards the table. I was ready for the dessert to come. As I got closer to my table I noticed a woman sitting down, not a bad looking one at that. She was wearing a white elegant dress. Her hair was light brown and her eyes were dark brown with long lashes. I sat down at the table.

"I hope you don't mind. Are you sitting here?" she said.

"Yes, I am" I replied "and now you are."

"Don't be angry with me but the restaurant is full and this was the only seat the waiter bought me over to" she said in a posh accent. "I'm Stella, nice to meet you."

Now to me this had Old Bill written all over it. I looked around the restaurant to see if I could notice her colleagues but no one seemed out of place but that's how the police like it. I looked at the woman again. She was kind of quiet. Now this doesn't happen often to me, rich women wanting to sit on my table, well not now any how. But what better way for the Old Bill to find out what I was up to? Planting a woman that could be a walking talking bug who could stand in the dock at court and give evidence far more advanced then the inventions today. Even they can't stand up in court. This was a set up. It didn't make sense to me, this woman just turning up out of the blue like this. Then it came to me, I thought the plan was the Scouser must have bought her with him and the plan was to get this woman to get in to my pants and get the money back while I was still asleep in the morning and leave me with the debt. Well I wasn't having none of it, if that was the case.

It turned out she wasn't either of the two. It turned out she was the owner of a jewellers. She told me while we ate our food. Her name was Stella. Her daddy had bought her the jewellers before he died, nice man. As we continued to chat she told me she was due to get married in the next three weeks, or so she said. She came across as a nice woman, but very posh. She had sex appeal that oozed from her. She was around thirty three and was looking good, if I may say so myself. This was the sort of woman you took home to your mum. Mum would be so impressed with her that she'd try marrying you off with her as soon as possible. We finished the meal and I paid for our food. Now I was one hundred and fifty quid flush from the Scouser leaving all that dough.

She thanked me and said it was very sweet of me to pay. I was charming her like a snake charmer does a snake and giving it plenty of Charley Large Potatoes and Billy Big Bollocks. Well why not push my luck after all. I did have 38 large on me and was wearing the Armani suit and was for now the owner of this new imported Japanese motor. So I was well looking the part. Even if it was just a blag for now to get in her pants, it seemed to be working.

Stella asked what I did for a living and I told her I was into sales. Well I was, so it wasn't a lie, just a twist of the truth. She was asking too many questions for my liking, jeweller's owner or not. So when she asked where I was from I continued with blagging her that bit more." I'm from all manors but mainly Edgware, darling".

She replied "Oh. I don't know that area. Is it nice?"

"It's OK," I said. I then got up and said "Excuse me sweetheart. I'll be back in two mins."

"OK", she replied. I walked towards the men's room but kept glancing back for some reason. I still didn't believe that this was a genuine thing that was going on or that she was who she said she was. She was oozing sex appeal and looked very sexy but in a very sophisticated way and the posh accent was really doing it for me. I left the table and went in to the toilet cubicle and got the devil's dandruff out, took a credit card out my pocket and pressed the corner of the card in to the powder and brought it carefully up to my nose. I sniffed hard as the powder shot up my nostrils and landed on the back of my throat leaving it feeling numb. I put the stuff away and came out back to Stella feeling a bit more confident now. I said, "Stella, sweetheart, I need to go."

"Yes, I need to be off too and getting back to the shop," she said. "It's been pleasant sharing lunch with you."

I asked her where the shop was.

She said, "It's in Oxford Street, not far from here."

I said "Would you like a lift?" pushing my luck that bit further.

Then she blew me out or so I thought as she replied "No thanks. It's not far. I can walk."

I was gutted even if I still thought she was a copper.

"You can walk me if you like as the traffic is dreadful at this time."

"OK, let's go".

The walk was pleasant and when we arrived at the shop I nearly fell over it impressed me so much, but I didn't comment on it. It had put my mind to rest that she wasn't a police officer and I felt more comfortable even if I now felt a little para from the line I'd just done back at the restaurant. A guard was opening the door to her shop so we could walk in. So pushing my luck that little bit further before I left her at the door I said, "We should do that again some time, Stella."

"Yes, that would be lovely. By the way what was your name again?"

"You can call me J. We should do dinner soon." I asked for her number and said I would call her when I was back in town.

"That would be marvellous, J." She lent forward and kissed me on the cheek. As she did, she blushed and so my head went off with loads of Charley thoughts from the line I'd had. Had she come in to my life at the right time to stop the Cruces in its tracks? She was due to marry in three weeks or that's what she said.

I walked back to the flash motor and started it up, with a deep growl from the engine and the twinned exhausts. I turned the stereo on from the controls on the steering wheel and the sound of Luther Vandross came on the C.D. The Scouser must have left in there. I edged out into the London traffic. The sun was shining down. I turned the stereo up a little and stuck my arm out the window as the electric slowly bought it right down. I started to head to Knightsbridge feeling on top of the world.

I arrived at Knightsbridge and dropped off the money. After that week I was unlucky enough to learn that money and drugs should never be in the same place at the same time. I was told to take the motor round the corner to a garage, whilst I was to go and sit in a pub, until the garage called me to pick it up.

After a while the garage rang told me the car was OK. Well, I knew that. The man then said I had to drive it down to Dover. I rang my firm and they said, **"IF THAT'S WHAT HE'S SAID, SON, THEN THAT'S WHAT YOU NEED TO DO. So go and do it and I'll take some more money of your debt. OK?**

So off down to Dover it was for me. It was getting late when I arrived there. I met a fella down by the docks who turned out to be a customs officer. Of all the people to meet, I had to meet him and I had no idea that he was one until he told me what he did for a living I handed him the case of money. He booked me into a hotel and said I needed to stay there for two days while he took the car. Well it didn't seem right to me. What was going on? Right or wrong? I was just doing my job and driving the motor to different people and dropping some money off. What could be wrong in that? Ask no questions, get told no lies.

Well, until I got the car back to Knightsbridge and the garage again this time instead of meeting the fella I'd seen I was told to go to a lock up where the car was to be parked. But when I got there the plans were changed. I met a fella and a woman in the lock-up. Inside there were three 4 by 4's waiting for the car I was driving to arrive. Why, yes you've guessed it. While I was innocently driving the motor to and fro, unknown to me the car was packed up with drugs. That must have come from the customs fella, and now was to be going out in these 4 by 4's. The car was jacked up. The bumper and half the fuel tank was dropped down, the spare wheel was cut open and there it all was, loads of the devil's dandruff. My guess was there must have been about 60 kilos of it. The car had been altered in such away to conceal all this. It was loaded in to the different 4 by 4's and off they went.

I asked what I should do with the motor. The man said I could use it for a week and then hand it back to my firm who would then give it back to the Liverpool firm. So now I had this motor for a week. How lucky can you get, until I got nicked for not having insurance and still having it unregistered plates. That's what you get for flashing it off.

It was job done and all I owed the firm now was £3000.

It was time to meet up with the nice posh Stella again. Well, things were going well with us keeping meeting up. Things were running as normal: powder in, powder out but as normal more powder went up my nose, when one night it came to me after I'd been out with Stella that this could turn out to be a nice little earner.

She was taking me back to her shop. Before I met her I had a sniff in the car. I got out with powder still in my nose like a neon light saying "Hey, I do cocaine." She noticed it straight away which was a bit embarrassing for me but to my amazement from then on she wanted some too so we were both now sniffing the devil's dandruff. At her shop, at lunch times. I'd go in to meet her. The guard on the door would greet me and let me in. I'd say hi to the other girl Stella had working for her and would go into the back. When the others went out for lunch I'd lock the door behind them and me and Stella would get sniffed up and start getting fresh with each other. Yes, the charm worked a treat with her and we would be all over each other chorusing and sniffing while the others were at lunch.

Then the earner was put into action. It was Friday afternoon. I had arranged for a friend to come with me to Stella's shop. He was briefed with what to do the night before. Well, it went like this. My friend stayed in the car watching me walk into the shop as normal. I was greeted by the security guard and the rest of the staff and Stella.

Stella told me to come in to the back where we began our ritual of coursing and sniffing also writing our names in the powder which we poured out on to Stella's desk. Stella told me to lock the door. This is where the plan came into play.

I walked to the door, clocking the cameras on me. I stood close to the door, and gave the thumbs up to my friend who was waiting patiently for his moment. I

pretended to lock the door and turned the sign to 'closed' so it all looked good to the cameras. I then walked calmly to the back to the office where Stella was waiting. As I walked in Stella was removing her pants, and letting down her hair and giving herself some D.I.Y. which was most inviting with stockings on.

Wow! As I turned her over and lent her softly over the desk, and started giving her some oral from behind. I then moved to gently taking her from behind. My action was now on the camera monitors watching the shop and not the job in hand. Stella wasn't aware of this, as she was now bent over the desk moaning loudly with pleasure so much so as she didn't hear the doorbell ring as it did when someone came into the shop. My friend came through the door with his rucksack. He walked calmly to the counter, lent down and pushed the panels to raise the glass lid where all the jewels were. After bringing one tray out he slid off his rucksack and filled it. Then he pushed the button again and the glass lid slowly closed.

He then walked calmly out of the shop. Now this had well put me off my stroke. "No!"

Stella was alerted and screamed "Don't worry, I'm on the pill."

What I really meant was "No!" to my friend for leaving the shop with only one tray. After all, these sort of earners don't come along again unless you're really lucky or as desperate as I was, back then in this circus of playing with the devil and his powder.

I didn't want to hurt Stella in any way and I knew she would be insured for some thing like this. We finished and as we got dressed I noticed there was also a camera in her office. I said "Stella, was that filming us?"

She smiled a little cheeky smile and said, "Yes of course."

Wow! What a little minx this rich girl had changed in to. I said "Best take the film out, sweetheart."

She told that it had been filming the shop front and her office at the same time.

I told her a video with what we'd been up to would be no good to a woman who was soon to be married. (With my pal coming in to help himself I guess the video was best in my hands!) I told Stella it should come with me or we should destroy it before it got into the wrong hands. Me meaning the Old Bill's.

I said goodbye to Stella and she told me that we should stop seeing each other as it was unfair on this fella she was soon to marry, which was handy as I didn't want to come back now the tray had been nicked. I said goodbye for the last time and walked out and got into my accomplice's car and he slowly drove off. Then I went to town on him. "Why only one tray?" I shouted.

"Er, well I heard moaning coming from the back and thought you were roughing her up so I left as quick as possible."

I had to laugh. He then leant over to the back seat and passed me the ruck sack. I unzipped the bag and pulled out the tray. There must have been about twenty rings of all different standards and types, some diamond ones, some gold ones, about £8000 worth of gems in all. But for us to sell or pass them on we'd only get back about £4000 or thereabouts.

We did get £4500 on them off some black market jewellers in Camden in the end but it was hard work trying to find a buyer. The tray was passed over and the gems exchanged for the cash. It was a deal for steel. The job was done. Every one was happy now the Queen's heads were stuffed into our pockets again. It's amazing what it feels like to know you've got a few quid in you pocket. It's like it gives you a little spring in your step and a bit of confidence.

Even Stella was happy. After all she did get married and she was insured so she didn't lose out, as she told me when I bumped in to her again in Bond Street, while she was shopping, which was a bit embarrassing. Not one of my best moves, but some times when push comes to shove some things need to be done, and with the devil on my back and his dandruff up my nose my morals and standards had taken a little back seat or they had for now. After doing the devil's powder it seemed like the right thing to do back then but there's no need to cry over spilt milk. That's what happened and that's what was done at the time. The film from Stella is probably well hidden in my pals porno collection.

Now I had money it was time to pay some of the dough I owed to Mr B which I did but only a monkey (£500). You're probably wondering why I didn't just pay all I owed off, and you're right, I should have, but I knew a small payment like that would keep Mr B happy for now and the parcels coming my way and I'd have a few quid in my pocket. You could say I was starting to do my first bit of juggling in the circus, which I was well and truly stuck into. I had left enough money by juggling with the drugs and dough for me to get away on a little holiday, or so I thought, with good friend of mine who came up with the idea that I needed a break from all this madness and stress that was going on around us. So it was off to Ibiza.

THE NIGHT BEFORE THE IBIZA HOLIDAY...

On this night, it was arranged that my entire little firm would all turn up in a restaurant for dinner in the village in the Wood. It was to be our last supper, because that was the last time the whole firm would be together at the same time.

The meeting was called to sort out who was to do what and have what with the drugs and money that belonged to one of Mr B's firm's which I was working for at the time. Also the gun that I'd ordered for Mr Ice had now arrived on the scene and it needed to be looked after and put in a safe place. Mr B's firm member was coming down some time in the week to collect payments owed but I would be away so all this needed to be sorted out before I left for Ibiza.

There were the good, the bad and the ugly in the firm: Treeny, Bones, and Lee. Lee wasn't ugly in his looks but in his behaviour, and if you got on the wrong side of him he could be very ugly indeed. Now these were my main members of my little firm that I worked closely with. They had their own little runners working for them but these were the main ones I dealt with.

Altogether in the whole firm there were six members. Two of them were girls. The two girls were well trusted and had been tested out in many ways to see where their loyalty stood. On many occasions they'd come up trumps when push came to shove and they were needed most.

I was sleeping with a girl who wasn't a firm member. We were sure she was passing info about me and us to the police because they always seemed to turn up wherever I was and where meetings had been set up. I learned that too much pillow talk when you're in bed with women could get you nicked or, even worse, info could go out to other firms so they could grass us up when they were pulled in or use on the streets so they could start making more money, or info could go to firms who we might have had a beef with. A lot can come out when you're laying in each others arms still sweating from doing the wild thing. That's why it's best to say nothing and just do the job in hand. Women in this game can be more deadly than the male so it's best they know as little as possible. It's safer for them and for yourself because many a time women have been known to have worked their way up the ladder, starting from sleeping with a foot soldier (a street seller), to sleeping their way right up to the top and trying to get to know the main players. It happens, believe me.

NOT every woman is like that, of course. I've met some very loyal women in my time who would give their life for the firm, and have. (No names need to be mentioned, you know who you are and respect to you all).

Treeny was also coming away with me to Ibiza. In fact it was his idea to go away in the first place. He said it would do me good to get out of the circus for a little bit and relax. Treeny wanted me out and away from it all. He knew it was bringing me down, and the people around me. He could see what this life was doing to me, but still I owed a large amount of money and I still needed my £1000 a week of sniff for myself as that was what I was now sadly sniffing. There wasn't a day when not one line ever escaped my nostrils.

Treeny had become much more than a friend to me. He has become more like a brother or one of the family. That's how I treated him, and I still do and that's how my family also treat him and his family to this day.

He was one of the only people of my little firm who looked out for me and I could trust. Whether in the street, or when I ended up in prison, his loyalty shone through without him wanting anything in return, just friendship back, which is hard to come by nowadays.

One night that really comes to mind when he showed me his loyalty was when a deal was sorted out between me and another little firm in Frogmore. Their firm had ordered little small parcels of drugs here and there which started to work its way up until they wanted a big drop which was a kilo of the devil's powder.

Now this night I'd gone to Mr B and ticked what they wanted from one of Mr B's people. The deal went off like this. I drove down in a black BMW 3251, which Mr B's big firm had got for me to work in. The parcel was put into the boot in a c.d. changer to hide it from the Old Bill if I was pulled. I then headed of to Frogmore car park to meet this other firm. It was dark in the car park as there were no lights. I parked up facing the entrance so I could see the lights of anyone who arrived. I turned off the engine and thought to myself that it would look a bit strange me sitting down there on my own. If the Old Bill did come down, they would definitely want to search the whole motor and if they did find the parcel then I'd be well in trouble. So I opened the boot, removed the parcel from the motor and walked between the lights shining from my motor towards the hedge in front of me, laid the parcel on the floor between the car's lights and pushed it into the bush out of sight. I then walked back to the car, switched off the headlights again and sat there waiting in the dark for the Frogmore firm to arrive.

Just after shutting the car door. I saw some head lights crawling slowly down into the car park then the flashing blue light went on. Yes, Old Bill had arrived, which was well lucky for me as if they'd been a minute earlier the circus would have come to an end.

They pulled up to the side of my motor. One got out and banged on my window with his torch. I pressed the button and it slid down.

"Hello mate, what you doing down here in the dark then?"

"Well, officer, I'm waiting for a friend of mine, to take him back to the Wood. He only knows how to get to this place and he don't know the rest of the way, so I 'm meeting him here and he says he'll follow me back."

"Ok, lad. We're going to search the car. Please step out and empty your pockets."

They searched the car and as luck would have they didn't find anything as I'd left it in the bush, a bit of sharp thinking on my behalf, I guess.

"Ok, sonny. Just be careful down here. It's not the best of places to be waiting for people."

"Bye" I said and off they crawled out the car park as slowly as they'd pulled in with the lights off. I thought how lucky could I get? If I hadn't had the brainstorm of hiding the stuff in the hedge I'd have been leaving with them and sitting in the cells waiting to be taken to court.

After the police had left a car's headlamps appeared again and it slowly pulled up to the side of my car. It was the Frogmore firm that I was waiting for. They were in a blue convertible Audi with blacked out windows. The car stopped right next to my car and two of the fellas got out just as it had been arranged. One of them jumped into the passenger seat of my car and then the other jumped in the back and slid himself across, so he was directly behind out of my sight unless I moved my rear view mirror. Then it all happened. The fella in the driving seat said "Do you have the devil's dandruff?"

I replied, "Yes, do you have the Queen's portraits?" meaning the money.

With that the fella in the front shouted at me, "Where 's the fucking gear then?" "Sorry" I replied.

The fella leant back to his pal then all out of the blue the fella in the back slid out a knife unknown to me and pushed it between my right side and the door and placed the blade against my side. Then he shouted again "If you don't tell me where it is you'll get hurt".

"So you'd better hurt me then" was my reply.

So he did. I felt the coldness of the blade as it pierced in to my skin and popped into my right side. I felt a sharp pain coming from deep inside the wound then the pumping of blood came rushing out. I could feel the pain with every heartbeat and I felt sick. The fellas in my car left me slumped over the steering wheel as they frantically searched the car and went through my pockets looking for the kilo of the devil's dandruff. Then they fled with empty hands, jumped into the Audi and sped off out of the car park and up the hill, leaving me there for dead or so they must have thought. I was blacking out and losing a lot of blood. I reached into my coat pocket. Now my breathing was getting shallow and my vision was starting to go bleary. I managed to push redial on the phone. The phone rang and rang. Was this going to be the end? No one answered. Would they find me dead in the morning? Well as luck would have it Treeny after some minutes, bearing in mind that it was three in the morning and a long shot. "Hello Treeny! Come quickly, mate. I've been done. I'm in Frogmore car park". I then blacked out again

"Hello you still there?" The phone went dead. The battery had runs out.

Treeny turned up and opened my car door. I was slumped almost on to the floor from the pain and bleeding from the wound. He said to me "Come, mate. Been sniffing the gear again?" as sometimes I'd get myself in to a right state sniffing all night long. Then he saw the blood coming from me, "Shit, Ginger! What the fuck..."

I came to and said "Look in the bushes over there." With that Treeny pulled me up and in to his car. He then went looking in the bush and stumbled on the kilo of the devil's dandruff. He picked up the bag and slung it in his boot then jumped in to the car and drove me to Barnet hospital. He booked me in and drove off, leaving the devil's dandruff at a girl friend's house by saying "Could I leave this bag of laundry here?" She was none the wiser what was in the bag so after making sure the devil's dandruff was safe Treeny came back to the hospital to see if I was OK.

They'd sewn me up by now and I was ready to go home, so he dropped me off and told me not to worry about the devil's dandruff and that he'd bring it back to me in the morning. Which he did and without any missing and without expecting a drink or a piece of it for his troubles. In my books he was a proper friend to stick his neck out for me like that when he could have taken the lot and I'd have been none the wiser. In this life there are a few people who are truly loyal and that you can trust with all your heart and believe me he was one of them.

Now five weeks had passed and it was time to catch up with the liberty taker who had stabbed me and tried to nick all the goods. I put the feelers out for him and within a week I knew where he lived, where his girlfriend lived and where he worked and drunk, which was all I needed to know. So now it was time to call in an old friend who owed me a long overdue favour. He was a traveller who could get his hands on vans as they do, which was handy for the job I had in mind. I met him at his campsite, which was a scary business in itself, but it was where he was staying, I told him I needed a van so I could take someone away and scare them. He said he was just the chive for the job so soon it was sorted out that we'd go and pick up this Frogmore firm's liberty taker and scare him by putting him in the van and taking him up the lanes, rough him up a bit and leave him there. It seemed pretty fair and minor considering what he'd done to me that night, when the deal should have gone off like clock work. But there's always someone out there who wants to be the hero, and see if they can get away without paying. Funny they never seem to weigh up the consequences beforehand or realise what comes around goes around, and it had come round a lot quicker than he'd thought.

We went to the Frogmore firm's fella's work place, pulled up and waited. I was in the back of the van with a balaclava on and my pal was dressed in a delivery uniform. We plotted up in the car park of the liberty taker and waited until he came out. Soon he was walking through the car park towards us. My mate spotted him from the photograph we'd picked up when we were finding out about him and where I could get my hands on him so my pal called him over to the van and said "Hi I've got a delivery for your work. It's a bit heavy so you couldn't give me a hand to carry it, could you?" With that my pal led him to the back of the van where I was waiting. He opened the door and I pulled the liberty taker in to the van and my mate pushed him in and hurled him to the floor. My mate slammed the doors shut, started up the van, drove out the car park and headed for the lanes. Now I was in the back staring through the holes in the balaclava with a cold stare looking right at the liberty taker. I pulled out the gun, which had been given to me from my pal in Mill Hill, the one that had been ordered for Mr Ice. I'd pushed it down the front of my jeans.

The liberty taker froze still had his head on the floor where I told him to stay. When we reached the Lanes, the back doors were opened again and I told him to get up and get out. We tied his legs to a tree and arms with some tow ropes. All the while he was saying "I haven't done nothing. Why are you doing this to me?"

My pal the traveller leant against the van with his arms folded. I stood back pointing the gun at him.

"Please, I ain't done nothing."

I said, "Do you know who I am?"

"No" he said.

"Well you fucking do now." I pulled off the balaclava and he was scared shitless. He begged.

"Man, I never meant to do that! They told me to."

I replied "Well they won't be telling you to do anything again, will they son?" I dropped the gun down to his foot and squeezed slowly on the trigger. Bang! The gun kicked back. The birds flew off as the echo went round the fields and came back to where it had left. My heart was pumping and I looked at the fella.

"Ah fuck, fuck! My foot!" he squealed.

Then my traveller friend started freaking out. "Shit, man. Fuck! You said you were only going to scare him. Fuck! Let's go." With that he ran round the driver's side of the van and jumped in and started the van up.

I looked at the liberty fella. He was in a right mess. I said "Do you have a phone?"

In between the pain he squealed "Yes, here, take it!" I took the phone and jumped into the van. The van's wheel's spun off and my pal looked at me all concerned. He repeated "I thought you were only going to scare him"

"Well" I said. "Did he look fucking scared?"

He laughed nervously, I rang the 1st number on the phone for some one to come and help him. We said no more to each other about it and haven't to this day. I did feel bad doing it but it was an eye for an eye in my book. So without Treeny being as loyal as he was I could have been out there still paying back what I'd lost as they would have taken. I would have been on the receiving end of a bullet, not from them, but from my firm for losing the cocaine. When it's in my hands it's on my head and my responsibility or I'd be left for dead where they'd stabbed me.

My little firm were all told what to do before me and Treeny left to go to Ibiza. Bones was given the gun to look after and a thousand E's and the rest were given puff and money to pay to the big firm when they came down to collect it. A taxi turned up and Treeny and me packed our cases into the cab.

When we arrived at the airport we went into the toilet, put about twenty E's into a glitter tube each and put them up our bums to take them to Ibiza. I guess that's where the saying comes "Up the Gary Glitter". I had five grams of the devil's sewn into my boxers. We sat down in the airport to have a drink, when Treeny said it was uncomfortable having the E's up our bums. I said I couldn't feel anything, then I realized why. The pills had fallen out, gone down my trouser leg and had come out and rolled about two feet under the table. Now this was a bit of hot water we'd found ourselves in as the police were walking around with machine guns three feet away from us. We tried to ignore the fact for a while then I calmly walked up, put my bags down and scoped the E's up just as if I'd found a tenner on the floor, and had to slyly pick it up. The pills were rescued and it was time to board the plane, so it was back to the toilet to plug the pills once more.

Once on the plane, I went straight to the toilet and opened a gram of the devil's and then Treeny came in and hoovered up some too before we sat in our seats. We sat down and waited for the plane doors to shut and we were off into the air with the captain speaking. "We are travelling at five hundred miles an hour at a height of four thousand and five hundred feet ".

That was when Treeny turned and said "I'm up a lot higher than that after that little toot." We laughed together and waited to land. Once we'd landed we went straight to the hotel, dropped our bags and then went straight to San Antonio. That's where the partying and raving began.

One night me and Treeny were in San Antonio when I found myself charged up to the max from the devil's dandruff that was constantly being abused (not unusual for me back then, but I was on holiday.) I'd met up with a beautiful dancer who was a sexy blond and Treeny fell for her mate who was also good looking. They were club reps. We shared some nights and some lines and we got chatting and instantly clicked. When I told one girl what I did in

England she laughed and said "You'll love my dad." She took me and Treeny to meet him after I'd made love to her on the beach across the road from the clubs while Treeny and her friend also got more acquainted. We then went back to her apartment - me, her friend and Treeny, and continued to sniff and do the wild thing. By this time Treeny had his girl's pants off too.

In the morning we woke up and the girl I was with had ordered two bottles of champs to go with breakfast, which went down a treat. She then said she'd like to introduce me to her dad who turned out to be the club owner. We'll call him Aladdin as he resembled him a bit. He owned two night clubs and was well connected all over the island. He was also connected to the time share business and the crooks that went with it. He was an old time bank robber who'd left England for his own safety. He had made it big on the island and was now a retired or semi retired smuggler in his spare time, not that he needed to be as he was cake boo himself. He had his fingers in a lot of pies. Well, I got to know him well through his daughter, and things moved on from there. He was doing a lot of business in London with his E's that they were being made up out here. They were being shipped to Manchester and some times smuggled into Liverpool through the docks. They were smuggling pot loads by the ton that they had packed into lorries. Also they were making a mint selling them all over the island, as it's well known for its club life. Smart holiday, I thought, as I looked from the villa's balcony and continued chatting with these villains I'd been introduced to. A rest from the circuses, or so I thought. In fact I was bang in the middle of someone else's circus .

Aladdin introduced me to his friends and they must have taken an instant liking to me particularly after

Aladdin's daughter mentioned a friend's name who I knew well back in London. The fella was a big time gangster himself who had good connections in Amsterdam and was running brothels and peep shows and sometimes he'd direct his own porno's when he wasn't debt collecting. The girls that worked for him treated him like a king. The villa that the dancer had taken us to, to meet her dad, was very impressive and had all the up to date mod cons and three very nice motors parked out side. A Bentley Convertible, an Austin Martin and a big Land Rover.

The villa had two swimming pools, a sauna, a jacuzzi and seven rooms. What a place! The man also owned a yacht, which was down by the docks and looked better then Robert Maxwell's. That is where we went next, me, his daughter, Treeny, her friend and her dad's three minders. We got on to the yacht and sailed across to another island. It was the same yacht that had come and met the Yardie brothers that time I was out in Jamaica, but I didn't say anything.

There were more of the man's firm on this island we'd come to. They had a villa all kitted out to press up their own E's. In another little villa we were shown to they had so many E's they must have been in their thousands, all in plastic bags and being boxed and money was being counted by machines on one side of the room. It looked like a factory on one side and on the other like a bank. They had a proper little chemist's there. They also had minders all over the gaff. I started feeling real nervous being in a place like this. For me it was a case of only certain people should see things like this or you only saw it on the movies but it was nice to be trusted, I guess, knowing Aladdin's friend the gangster in London had probably had me checked out before we were shown all this.

Now this was Charley Big Potatoes! All this was well out of my league. I felt excited knowing that not many people in life would get to see stuff like this, only maybe in films. Not that some people would want to, but it was scary and exciting all at once. Before long we left and were back on the yacht: me, Treeny, the dancer's friend, her dad and the two minders. The others stayed in the villa. We decided to leave her dad so the speed boat that was on the side of the yacht was dropped into the sea and before long we were speeding back to Ibiza through blue water. We parked the speed boat up, climbed out on the docking bay and sat in a bar drinking and doing E's and sniffing cocaine.

Being with the dancer made it easier to get into clubs, some without paying.

Drugs were a way of life in those clubs. A week of clubbing passed and it was time to say goodbye to the friends and girls we'd met and head back home to England to recover. But after a holiday in Ibiza you need another to get yourself together again.

When we arrived back at my house I realised there was new glass in the door window and a size 12 footprint was still stuck on the door where it had been kicked off. It had been the police. They had come unexpectedly one early morning, raided my mum's house and found an ounce of cannabis and seven wraps of white powder. They wanted to arrest my mum for them so I went and told the Old Bill they were mine. The wraps were from a party and were found in a coat on the banister so it was best to say the coat weren't mine. Well, it might not have been.

The police had also raided Bones and found the Harry Hooter and once they found that they stopped looking. Lucky because they left the E's safely unnoticed where he'd hidden them. They told him they knew the gun was mine and that if he told them it was they could arrest who they really wanted but he just said "No comment" so for some reason they let him off with a warning. He had a little help from his solicitor who told him what to say to get off the best he could. He was well lucky.

Before long I found myself going on another holiday but not the sort with sunny beaches and topless women, but a holiday at the Queens Hotel, I mean Wood Hill Prison. It was well different to the hotels I'd been in before. That's where I did the nine months where the Iceman and me met up again as you read about earlier. The thing with prison is you come out knowing more about criminal activities than when you went in and of course that's where more contacts are made.

Well, I'd done my bit of porridge and it was time to move on from the circus. It had stopped for a short time while I was in prison but soon came along again, sooner than I thought. I'd been picked up from prison by Mr B, and as you've guessed, he still wanted what I owed him, but that was told to me after the partying and sniffing that went on for three days as a token of me being free and back with the firm.

GOING STRAIGHT:
It Weren't For Me

After the partying had stopped I thought it was time to leave the circus behind me, start a normal job and do normal things or at least learn to appreciate them. It lasted all of two weeks before old customers were asking me for the devil's dandruff. As normal the circus started all over again with me taking the devil's myself and ticking it off Mr B. But now this time I'd met a few contacts and had started to juggle with each firm's money. It was working out well or as well as could be for now. I'd tick from Paul to pay Peter and tick from Peter to pay Paul, as the saying goes. In other words I was juggling in more ways than one just to stay on top and it was working out at the moment.

I'd been given a job by a friend who was working the door at the film studios. So more and more contacts were made and it was easier to deliver what the customers wanted and be chatted up by the birds at the same time, also to take what drugs they'd bought with them and sell them back in to the club later on. I managed to become friends with the manager of a strip bar and the doormen would welcome me in and make me feel comfortable. One of the doormen became a good friend and would welcome me with open arms every time I turned up to the club.

There were women all over the gaff in his club showing off next to nothing, shimmering around the poles and bunny girls coming to the table for drinks, and girls coming up for dancing. My sort of place! Maybe I should make this my local, I thought. It's amazing what a beautiful body can do dancing in its full glory two inches from your face. It's like being hypnotised by the snake out of the Jungle Book.

When I was at the club they'd make a point of looking after me. After all, I was there for their interests as well as my own. I got on well with the management and they'd let me in free with a golden handshake with half of the devil's in my hand as a little token of my appreciation for the way they looked after me and any guests I'd bring with me. They'd also walk me through the changing rooms to meet the girls, so I could sell some more devil's to them. I got to know them on a more personal level which was all very nice and some times if I was well lucky I'd end up in the club at the end of the night with cocaine all over the show and all over my face. The women would help themselves to the devil's that was spread out on mirrors I'd delivered with a few kilos to the management which had been paid for by their firm.

The two girls who were there made me laugh. Charlie and Amanda were proper funny friendly girls. They worked behind the bar and never stripped which gave me more respect for them, not that I didn't respect all the girls. Being in there you can't go wrong with an eye full of tits and a piece of fanny two inches from your nose. It beats watching football and it's better than a packet of peanuts.

There weren't much bragging or speaking in these sort of clubs. It wasn't no back street seedy place but an upmarket sort of gaff where a lot of face would come to talk, have fun, relax and enjoy the night's dancing.

It was more pleasure than business but a few business meetings did go down here. I'd met up with Treeny this night. When I was with him I was less likely to use cocaine, well at least try to, anyhow. A good looking stripper cosied up to me. Not that they weren't all good looking but you tend to know which ones you like the best, so she came over, sat down, said a little speech and told me her false name. Before long she had her kit off and her bum in my face. Nice girl! I said "Does your dad know that you're doing this"?

She winked and giggled and said "No, but my mum does." The girls were witty and full of charm and I liked them for that. I liked them all, oh yes. We got chatting after the dance and started to get to know each other on a more personal level. Probably because I'd written my name and phone number down on a fifty-pound note and pushed it into her pants after the dance she gave me. It turned out she wanted some devil's as she whispered in my ear while dancing "Hi honey! Got any powder?" It would be this night of all nights when I had none around me because I'd been juggling so much with everyone's money and drugs. I'd paid off Peter but at the same time Paul wanted his dough too, which left me without any powder, and without a debt unless I ticked some more.

Well until I went off with the stripper. So now I was in trouble but as Lady Luck was on my side I'd taken a chance and it all worked out in the end. Lucky it did. It turned out that the stripper had wanted to see me after the night's stripping for some devil's drandruff and a personal chat. But I wasn't in my manor and far from my contacts. Well, not this time in the morning anyhow. So even if I tried I couldn't get any devil's even if I wanted too.

The stripper came out of the changing room, with a nice big fur coat on and walked with the coat swaying just off her shoulders and flashing a very little dress indeed.

Also her long blond hair was swaying from left to right and her big round firm boobs were bouncing up and down. She had a little spring in her step. It was the sort of picture you'd see on Baywatch and David Hasselhoff would have been proud of. The coat was just hanging off her shoulders, flashing not much on underneath apart from a silk short dress that hugged her hourglass figure. She came bouncing over to me and Treeny. We were shaking hands with the bouncers at this point and thanking them for the good night we'd had. Then all three of us left, me, Treeny and the stripper who I'd learnt was called Sam. As when we left the bouncer said "Bye Sam", kissed her cheek and winked at me with a grin.

As we got outside the strip club the Jack Daniels started rushing to my head, I knew a line of the devil's dandruff would knock it back into place. I explained to Treeny that I'd been invited back to the stripper's house and I'd meet up later the next day at the Horse and Wagons in Dunstable, where their happy hour was a pound a strip not a pound a pint!

After a little while Treeny agreed to go home and put an end to the good night we'd just had. So I phoned for my driver to come pick him up from outside the club and take him home. In the meantime Sam and me had walked round to the car park to get her car. We were heading towards a brand spanking new Mercedes. This car was a proper tool! These girls were earning a fortune or her fellow was, one of the two. As she pushed the alarm, the doors popped open and we both slid in on the leather seats.

Then it came straight out, as bold as brass. "Got a line then, mate?"

With my tail between my leg, I said, "Sam, look, sweetheart. I ain't got any and I'm trying to give it a rest".

Who was I fooling, her or me? Well, I guess the night was finished before it had began as it went silent.

"Well, we'd best get some then", came Sam's reply. "I know just the place but before we go lets roll a spliff".

I did this from the skunk she had which was in her dashboard. As she started up the roaring engine I took off my jacket and flung it in the back of her motor. The stereo was turned on and the song playing was the garage tune "Pretty Green Eyes". I noticed a bottle of champagne was lying on the back seat. "What's this then, Sam? You a secret lemonade drinker?" I joked.

"Open it up if you want" she replied. "Don't be shy." So I did. Then we shot off towards Chinatown, smoking the spliff out of the window, chatting and giggling from the smoke and the sips of champers that we were sharing. We arrived at Chinatown and pulled down some poorly lit street, parked the Merc up and jumped out. Now I couldn't wait to get a line up my nose. It's weird once you feel the alcohol then you feel like a line. I guess they go hand in hand some times like sex and a fag afterwards. My head was also a little buzzing by this time from the Jack D's back at the club.

It must have been about 4.30am by now in the morning. Sam led the way and we went into an open Chinese restaurant. There sitting in front of me was a small Chinese geezer just a bit bigger than the fellow out of the Bond movie, the one with the bowler hat, and he did look pretty similar too. He had some Chinese writing up both hands and he was just eating noodles from the bowl. He had a diamond ring on his finger that the Queen would have been eyeing up *or* would have liked. "Hi, Wong! Long time no see, hey?" Sam ran over and cuddled him. He raised his eyes slowly.

It reminded me of when I used to get some pot from an old friend of mine, in fact a very loyal good friend for many years. I was 25 at the time. I nicked-named this fella Mr Myagi like the geezer out of Karate Kid. When I called on him for the odd bit of herbals or pot he would shuffle slowly to his door, open it real slowly and have trouble opening his blood shot eyes to see me on his door step, as he'd be well stoned. When I spoke he would say "Yes" after he'd regained his focus and speak in a slow deep lazy voice and by nodding his head say "yes" as if he knew what I was saying. Then he'd say "Yeah, er, sorry mate. What did you say again? We'd crack up laughing and that was when we weren't talking in code to each other on the phone to stop the police who might have been tapping our phones so they wouldn't know what we really meant or were saying to each other. You'd tell Mr Myagi something and he'd say "What did you say again?" after really thinking hard about whatever was said. At the time it didn't matter as his head would be somewhere else and his mind would be well far away in his stoned state. He'd need a re-cap later on what was said that night or day. Anyhow, when he'd come down he'd always recap about what had been discussed so he could keep on the ball with what was going on in the firm. It was a Mork calling Orson turn out, like in Mork and Mindy when Mork calls on Orson's conscience to find things out for him whilst standing in the cupboard. Proper far out, man? He was a proper good friend, one you can rely on when you're stuck in a sticky position or in Her Majesty's prisons! I respect him endlessly and his family too. He makes the word loyalty seem small. The amount of loyalty and respect he's shown my family and me over the years and still continues to do so - there's only a few mates you can count on one hand but he's on there.

The other close friend I had was my dad, who sadly passed away while I'm writing this. He's greatly missed by us all, and although I may not have shown it in my action I loved and miss him dearly. I loved listening to him, and also to my Nan, who passed away four months before. She'll always be remembered. She always had time for me and even saw round the rascal I was when I was younger. Well most of us were. Not forgetting my mum, who is a true friend indeed, a strong fighter and has helped me endlessly. There's nothing in this world I could do to pay her back. I just have to be there for her to as she has for me. Not forgetting my brother in Liverpool and his family. And Mr Adams and his family too. I would also class Paul as one of those friends you would count on your hand and rely on in times of great importance.

So my mind drifted back to this Chinese fella, Mr. Wong whom Sam and me had met in China Town. Mr Wong was connected to a Triad firm, which had just come over from the Middle East and set up some businesses here in London. All this I found out later when I was paying off debts that I owed Mr. Wong. I'll tell you more about it in a minute or when we get to that part!

Mr WongWong stared at me with squinting deep green eyes and said slowly "Who is this stranger, Sam? Why have you bought him here?"

"This is a good friend of mine. I wouldn't have brought him here if he wasn't recommended and if he wasn't safe. Wong, come on! You must know me by now."

"Why have you come, Sam?"

"I need some cocaine, Wong. Why else would I be here?"

With that Wong said to the barman "Get my phone." This geezer came over who was well shaped like he worked out. It looked like he belonged in the London Dungeon, in the torture chambers as one of the executioners. He passed Wong the phone and Wong spoke in Spanish. I just heard and picked up the last sentence as I'd learnt a little Spanish from some smart fella that I shared a cell with once, banged up in the boof. The sentence went like this, I think. "Tell the family I send my best and to the cartel too." Then he put the phone down and said "It'll be here soon Sam."

A man about five foot six and stern looking with mouse blond hair and a deep husky voice came into the restaurant. His name I learnt later on but more about Old School later. He was dressed in motorbike leathers, and he had a green rucksack over his right shoulder. He removed his motorcycle helmet and walked towards Wong. "Hi Wong" he said. "Senior, how's tricks, you cockroach?"

Wong laughed and then Old School put the rucksack on the table in front of Wong. Then the Old School said "I'll see you again later on." As he walked slowly out he stared straight at me, directly into my eyes. Our eyes met and I could feel the coldness in them which sent chills down my spine. The man wasn't Spanish. He just liked people to think he was or certain people until you got to know him on a more personal level. In fact he was far from Spanish but could pass easily for one and spoke the language fluently. For some strange reason I knew we'd meet again, but on good terms I hoped. It wasn't long before we did.

Before long Wong was pulling open the rucksack that had been left. He slid out about four kilos of Colombia's finest. He told the London Dungeon geezer to bring over a silver tray, which he did. Then the geezer locked the door to the restaurant and pulled the blinds closed whilst slowly peering out the window. Then he walked back behind the bar and into the shadows again. Wong rested one of the glass blocks on the tray, then cut at the plastic bag. It opened and Wong then broke off a big chunk and crushed it into powder. Then he made three fat lines up, pulled out a gold charley tooter from his pocket and gave a new name to the Dyson Hoovers as the line in front of him disappeared up his nose. Then he pushed the tray towards Sam. She leant down, moved her long blond hair to one side, took up her line and sniffed hard. She held her nose as she raised her head from the tray the lady way. Then she pushed it to me. I looked at Wong and he nodded with the appreciation that I was looking for. So without delay I picked the tooter up and sniffed up the line that had been put there for me.

Wow! After that line I felt like Hercules and my mind was rising. My heart was skipping beats, my mouth was numb, and the back of my throat and my gums. Wow, the eagle had landed! I felt on top of the world and far away from my dizzy state that the Jack Daniels had put me and Treeny in, back in the club an hour ago. Wong broke off a chunk, which must have been about an ounce and a 1/2, and put into a see-through plastic bag and he passed it to Sam. "There you go, girl. That'll be £1500, OK?"

Sam looked at me and it came out that Wong was pointing to me. I had no money, only five quid, as the night's drinking at the club had restricted my funds until I could get working back in the manor or collect in a few debts. "Wong" I said, a bit embarrassed, "I don't have the money right now."

"Well," he said, standing up from his chair, "I'm running a business, not a charity. Take it and find it. What else have you come here for, son?"

"OK" I said.

Sam then said "Let's go."

So we did. I left their £1500 debt. I was a proper sucker for the women back then. Aren't we all? I shook Wong's hand and thanked him. As we left, I told Wong I'd be back.

He said, "I know you will be, son" as he held my hand in the shaking position for that bit longer and held it tighter looking in to my eyes.

Then we said goodbye. "Nice to meet you, Wong".

Sam and me headed back to hers. Wong had me followed that night, which I didn't know until it was time to pay the money back to him for the devil's. He told me everything I'd done that night. But now I'd shown him some respect by coming back to pay him instead of him looking for me. Which was a rarity as you would normally have to hunt your money back if you had ticked it to certain people. After that day I paid him, I was able to tick the finest of cocaine from Wong and be like Mr B, or near enough. Now I was getting the devil's finest and at much less than what I was used to. For the quality it was, it meant it could be stamped on twice and still be about fifty five per cent on the street or around about that, give or take a bit. This put me in a better level to do business.

We got back to Sam's and one thing led to another and before I knew it we had sniffed the lot. Her nice flat mate and me. Sitting there in Kensington we'd sniff the morning and night away with no action in the trouser department. Something even weirder happened that night. The paranoia started to creep in and the grim reaper kept appearing every time I had a line or two. It turned me into Laurel and Hardy in one body as it messed with my mind.

What happened to feeling like Hercules and being on top of the world, or Charley Large Potatoes and every one thought you were the bollocks and a right party animal and all you said was important and every one wanted to hear it. Right now it was just mumbling to yourself about conspiracy theories. Well them days had long gone as I had caned so much cocaine and every time I started to do a few lines the grim reaper would turn up on his impending clouds of doom. After a few lines I'd turn into Laurel and Hardy and my speech would go all funny like Bugs Bunny "Wha……..what's up doc?" It was far from feeling like Hercules that I used to feel. More like a scared mouse. I'd be thinking that everyone was out to kill me and out plotting large conspiracies against me, even the people who were close to me. Well they weren't, far from it, looking back at the things I got into. There are a lot of jealous people that think they're your friends out there but can't wait to see you fall.

That night I learned money can't buy you love, as these girls had many a geezer flashing the cash at them and sniffing cocaine around them all night. Well almost every night. I was just one of many.

Police stalk, as the money talks when you juggle in the circus of the devil's powder

Well now I had Wong as my contact I could tick good quilted gear for half the price, much cheaper than I was given it by my firm and from Mr B's. And it would be in one piece and not repressed but at a pressed price as they were bringing so much over. We were now able to work with other firms throughout London, as the devil's powder we were now getting was of top quality. So now money was coming quick and fast so much so it was getting hard to hide the facts of what we were doing even with money laundering. The hardest thing in this game is to hide the money when there's so much of it and so much of it ain't even yours. Well, the more you have, the more you want to spend. So we were all giving it large. Blowing money in clubs. Staying in top London hotels with women. Sniffing as much as we liked with pals and the real villains we were making a mint for. We were living a limousine life style and living like pop stars. Sniffing all night long and all day long if we wanted. Without a dent in anybody's pockets for a change. We were all buying name brand clothes, Gucci and Armani suits. Going to casinos and the odd flash restaurant here and there. Blowing money like we had shares with the royal mint.

We were giving it Big Potatoes to every one we met. We all looked the part in our nice new cars and clobber. We would all be flash with our gold and platinum diamond rings and bracelets. Well, you couldn't miss them sparkling off our arms. Who could blame us? We'd worked hard for it and risked our liberty every day to so why not be a little flash now and then? The firms were paying drivers to drive me around London to deliver their goods to clubs and other firms and places. They were buying me cars so I could go from a to b to collect money and deliver their merchandise, not necessarily drugs all the time.

We spent loads of money on drinks putting it up our noses, and on club strippers and prostitutes and massage parlours. Just generally having a good laugh and dodging the Old Bill now and then even though they enjoyed following us into the clubs and places we went, and the back handers they were given were well apprciated whether directly or in direct. We'd be buying what we wanted when we wanted it without having to look at the labels of things to judge if we had enough to buy them and not get nervous when we got to the cashier on the till. Sometimes the price came back at you like an upper cut. "That'll be £3000, sir." 3000 grand! (Well, I nearly fell over. Well, we were in Harrods). When we had no money I'd have to put the item back and pretend I was looking for something a bit more in my league. Just to show a bit of face. Now now just pay and put the item in the bag not back on the shelf no worries.

It was good meeting new people and firms every day or different people who were or weren't connected, or had their fingers in different pies. It seemed there was always something to do, someone to meet or a place to be back then and it made you feel real important but all for the wrong reasons.

We were paying black cabs to drive to the airport to pick people up with luggage that cost us £5000 to bring back. The police were getting closer to the things that were going on. They knew something and we were tipped off from a few that were on the books or had been. After all they were turning up in strange places in plain clothes, just to find out bits and bobs, and witness what was going on and to collect there back handers. Even when things weren't going on they would still be there looking over our shoulders. Also to find out who knew what and what was going where, pulling in different people for other crimes and building a bigger picture. So the police were waiting for the right time to come get us or for us to mess up so they could have us bang to rights and be able to hit us with a large lump of bird.

We were living it large. Sometimes you felt larger than life and at other times you felt sick as a dog, but like most things they had to come to an end. Which they did when Wong introduced me to a fella called Old School. The story with Old School was that he had started working in someone else's manor in South London, so you could say he was stepping on a big firm's toes, which wasn't the done thing. But he didn't care.

The firm whose toes that he was stepping on had arranged to meet up with him without him knowing. They were going to pick him up unannounced in a drunken Jack Daniel's state with whitened nostrils, outside the Emporium nightclub, in a limousine he thought was for him and his girl. Well it was for him, but not for his girl. It came with two gangsters to keep him company sent by the firm he had upset. They persuaded the girl it would be better for her to get a cab home and leave Old School with them as he had business that needed sorting out.

They'd showed off to the girl he was with that night outside the club after he'd been out on a mad binge with a few old faces he knew. Some nice looking women were there and the odd celebrity, one of the true gangsters that were talked about earlier. We'll call him Mr Uncle Dave C. That's what Old School liked to call him. The two gangsters who had picked Old School up outside the club took him back to the room the old faces had booked at the Savoy in London.

After a little roughing up they told him that for his own good he'd best disappear out this manor, faster than he'd appeared. Otherwise he'd find himself getting seriously hurt or in a bad accident or floating down the Thames or the River Lee. This was a friendly warning with no one getting hurt, just yet. All of a sudden Old School stood up to confront these two gangsters. As he thought now he was Hercules after the drink and Charley, in a drunken state he said "You'd better get your pals together then or the real faces that have sent ya."

"OK, that's it" said one of the gangsters after banging him in the jaw onc more time. "I've had enough of this piece of shit and his small talk. Something must be wrong in your head, Old School." They knew who he was but he didn't know them from Adam. Well, if you're in the know you're in the know, and people think they know you or have heard of ya, even before you had. The gangster put his hands down his trousers, pulled out a shooter, and put it to Old School's head. The other gangster calmed the other one down and said "It's too messy in here to do that".

"You're a walking dead man" the man with the gun continued to say to Old School, but put the gun back where he'd pulled it from. "You'd best get your head out of your arse and be back together for tomorrow." They'd be seeing him again, and the real twins that were running the manor at the time would be with them.

Old School replied "Listen. Call it all on. I want to meet them at the old horseracing track round by Walthamstow."

"We'll be there, Old School. Don't you worry, son."

"Yeah. Yeah. Now no drama, old boys," Old School said jokingly. "I'm not going nowhere. I'll be there." Old School hadn't realised he'd just created a war. The gangsters left and Old School did the last line he'd saved for himself on the marble table in front of the bed, to stop the pain he was feeling from the digs he'd been given. He switched his mobile off, took his Cartier watch off his achey arm, looked at the time and collapsed on the huge bed a bit sour where he'd been roughed up a bit. The room had already been paid for by the old twins who'd had Old School picked up as a V.I.P. Liberty, Old School thought, as he drifted off to sleep after the coke had worn off. Well. Old School could talk. He was used to taking liberties himself. That was one of his traits. He swore by them. I was on the back end of a few with some bad deals he'd set up and with a few cars I'd lent him now and then. "If you're going to take a liberty then take a big one, as you get the same thing for it" he'd say, and he had with many people, who'd shown him kindness. But morals and standards mean more than money.

To me he took many people's kindness for weakness and like most people came unstuck a few times. I think the firms only kept him alive that long because he owed so much money. Old school knew once he had paid his debts to the firms he was a walking dead man. When you owe money it sometimes keeps you alive, 'cos if you're dead you can't pay it back, can ya? And if no one knows who your family are, how can they get to them? Some people would just put a bullet in him and wipe their mouth of the money. Well, these people were out of my league, for now anyhow, but they were out there.

Old School woke up early, ordered breakfast in bed, phoned up his old pal, who he'd served in the army with, and who'd now turned hit man and arms dealer in his spare time. While chewing on some toast Old School asked him to join him for breakfast at the Savoy hotel so he could organise some sort of reassurance for the long day ahead. He was to face a sawn off shot gun, and a full length leather jacket, which the hit man had bought with him, and left in a car in an underground car park where some knuckle fights used to go on. Nice friend, eh? It's good to know you have friends who'd risk their life for ya or their liberty, or would go the extra mile for you in the time of need.

So Old School got kitted out in the underground car park where they'd arranged to meet. Old school then thanked his pal, cuddled him, kissed his cheek on either side, got in his jag and drove off through London without a care in the world to the tracks to meet the two old time faces. Old school parked the car with the front end facing the way out and the only way in. He got out calmly and sat on the bonnet concealing the sawn-off in his full length leather. He looked like something out of the Matrix with his Italian shoes, blacked out Armani glasses, full length Moschino leather jacket and his hair brushed back into a pony tail. A black Saab pulled in slowly, and came to a halt about five metres in front of Old School's car. In the front were two minders. In the back were the two men Old School had met at the hotel. They were staring at Old School.

Before they had time to take off their seat belts or even move Old School pulled back his leather jacket as fast as lightning and pulled out the sawn-off. With two quick flicks of his finger he pumped both shells from both barrels in to the facing car. Bang, bang! As the noise echoed around them one bullet hit the driver and the other hit the passenger. Blood splattered on to the windscreen like a burst water melon. Old School slowly walked a bit further towards the facing car, as the two old faces try to scarper out of the back seat of their Saab. As they both got out and tried to run for their lives at the same time as trying to get their guns out, Old School felt in his deep leather jacket pockets for two more shot gun shells. As the old faces ran off into the distance Old School pulled the trigger again and delivered two more bullets. One of the faces hit the floor dead while the other clutched his leg and tried to hop off. Old School concealed the still smoking barrels of the shotgun by putting them back into his jacket, walked over to the old face trying to get away and said "This is my manor, and I'll work where I like, and you or no one will tell me any different". After that he removed his foot from the old face's back, then walked away from the scene as calm and collected as if he'd just opened a Swiss bank account with loads of doggy bonds. He then got into his jag and drove to a nearby building site, where he tossed the gun into the still wet concrete that had been just laid. He watched it sink, never to be seen again, he hoped. And it ain't been found so far.

So now you know why the police were stalking us. You can't blame them really can ya, now there were loads of dead bodies everywhere. But the police just looked at it as another gangland killing, three less scumbags they'd have to worry about, and they'd brush it under the carpet. It would all be forgotten about with in a week. But not by the villains. That little story was around for a long time and still is today. After that Old School had earned the respect from other firms in the surrounding manors as it seemed he had more arsehole than a lot of them. My motto was they liked me for me, not what I could scare them with.

So now Old School could now dance in all the manors and no one would say a thing, because talk was cheap and actions speak louder than words. But firms were getting tired of him and the liberties he'd started to take. And like most of us, he was falling under the spell of the devil's dandruff and it was corrupting him fast, so much so he was now juggling with the bigger firms' money and becoming unreliable and a liability. Like most people in this game the powder had corrupted him so much so that soon he'd ticked from every small firm in North London and was juggling with a few big ones in South London to pay back what he owed. He now owed large amounts of money, so much so he had to juggle to stay ahead, and the juggling didn't end for him and probably still goes on today. That's if he's around. So that was Old School's little story anyhow.

Once we were introduced Old School and me seemed to get on. We knew some of the same villains and it seemed our connections crossed in other ways. We were in the same position only he was juggling on a bigger scale in London by now. He soon introduced me to some parts of his manors. But with me working in my manor there was no room for him to work there too. Hence the saying "There's no room for jugglers in my circus".

Now we were hanging around together I'd work in the Wood and he'd watch my back and I'd do the same in his manors and in his areas around Neasden and Wembley and Cloisters Wood and other parts of London. I'd watch his back while he collected money and he'd come with me to collect mine. I also used to do a bit of bouncing for him in Cloisters and Sparkles wine bar, where he used to DJ now and then and at the radio station he worked in or for. Back then I had every bitch knocking down my door. So we worked in his manor and did a few things here and there.

One time there was someone that owed him money, so Old School went to a morgue and got a dead body out - as his uncle worked there - put the body into the back of his car and drove to Epping Forest Country Club where a plastic gangster friend wasn't paying a large debt. It was quite a lot of dough, about £50,000. He could have shot him, but you can't go killing everyone, can ya? You have to try and be a bit of a diplomat. So me and Old School thought we'd teach this fella a little lesson by driving to Epping Forest Country Club where he used to drink and was pretending to be a proper face, until we turned up and taught him a little lesson.

So I got in Old School's car and on the way to Epping Forest Country Club, I said "How you going to sort this fella out, then?"

Old School replied "Well don't worry, Mr Caveman. I've got a little reassurance in the boot mate that's going to straighten this right out". I've heard that saying somewhere, before I thought. To me it meant he had some shooters in his boot, and me and Old School were going to make a mess of this gangster. He was going to get it. I was thinking it would turn into a war, us going up to the club with shooters concealed in out coats, looking like John Wayne and giving it plenty of bollocks. It could turn out to be a war with the sort of clientele that would be at the club and with the bouncers even if I knew one or two of them, or had been introduced to them from when I'd done time or through other faces, or when I worked on the door at Sparkles and the Aces in Peckham.

This club was promoted by myself. I ran it for some time and I'd made Old School my DJ. A bloke called Martin was the dancer as me and him had hit the E's hard and gone mad on dancing all night long when we were there. It was Dave the harts local venue we called him Hart as he had a way to the women's heart he was a proper magnet where the ladies were concerned. He was like pimp daddy with all the women hanging off his arm and if you didn't find him there he would be at Rudolfs, that's where I met the wild K. I met the most outrageous and rude lady, the wild K at rudolfs who was pregnant with the new addition to the family, little Cookster Huggie G. She was one of the Wendy's who stood by me why in prison. She weren't always bad.

I said to Old School "What you want a war? Cos that's what's going to happen."

He told me "Don't worry son. I'll show him and the rest will just hear about it and be on their guard."

We pulled in to the car park. I was starting to feel nervous scared like I always did before I sorted anyone out, or if I knew there was a bit of trouble coming my way. I'd always try to be a bit diplomatic before the violence, if I could. We got out the car. My eyes were scanning the whole place like the front of Knight Rider's car, left to right, right to left. We walked up to the door and I shook hands with the bouncers and Old School and me walked into the club. Everyone was having a good time dancing as we walked through the crowd towards the bar. When we got to the bar Old School ordered two Jack D's. They came and Old School asked if Franky was in the club. The barman said he was upstairs in the V.I.P. Lounge so we walked calmly up to the V.I.P. Lounge.

We walked past the bouncer with a nod from Old School and we walked in and scanned the lounge for a few seconds, looking at the hot ladies dancing and showing off their cleavage and shimmying around. There were various faces and villains all around us but no Franky. Then old school spotted a very busty brunette with two big minders sitting on one of the sofas chatting and having a good time. The brunette turned out to be one of Frank's girls.

"Where's Franky," Old School asked.

"Why, who wants to know?"

"I do" said Old School. "So where is he?"

The minder turned round and faced us. "Who are ya?"

"Easy, boys" said the brunette.

"He's in the loo," the other girl said. That was near to here.

"Yea, OK darling. Thanks." So off Old School and me went after putting our Jack D's on to their table in unison. We headed to the toilets but when we got in there was still no sign of Franky until we heard giggling and sniffing coming from the cubicles, so we walked over to them. There were three cubicles - I went in one at one end, and Old School went in the third.

We looked over from our cubicle to see Frank. He was in the middle cubicle with a blond girl. His trousers were down and there was sniff on the toilet seat.

"Hello frank. Hope your misses don't walk in on ya she'd have something to say about this if she saw you like that." Old School said, spoiling the moment. "What's that, a chipolata hanging out?"

"Shit" Frank replied as he pulled his trousers back up. "Stop!" he said to the bird. "Go back to the table. I'll catch up with you in a second."

She wiped her nose from one of the lines Frank had pulled out for her. Now we were there Frank had best pull out some more. As Old School told him by saying "Ah, what's that on the toilet, Frank?" as if he didn't know. "Ain't that nice? Are those for me and my mate?"

"Oh that's nice, Franky" I said. "You must have known we were coming."

"Can't you see I'm busy, boys?" Frank said.

"Cant you see I'm getting tired of this shit, Franky?" Old School replied.

"Come back another time, fellas" Frank said. "You can see I'm busy."

"Not too busy to pay my money back, I hope, hey Franky" Old School said. "You'd best come outside."

"Don't worry son, I've got your money but not here."

"So where the fuck is it then because I really need it and I don't want this to get messy."

"Just a few more days."

"Outside Frank. I've had enough of you and your bollocks and false promises."

So we walked out the toilet after we'd all powdered our noses. Franky ushered his two minders to come out to the car park with him.

"Come over to my car," Old School told Franky. I've got something to show
you in my boot."

I was thinking it was the shooters and he'd be popping this Frank and the minders right here right here and now. As we all got closer to the car boot Old School opened it. We all stepped back and peered in to the back. Old School pulled back the cloths, and there in his boot was the freshly dead body. "Wow, what the fuck?" he said, knowing full well what it was as we could all see it.

"Shit man" came from the minder's mouth, but Frank just stared at it and looked sleeplessly white as his knees quivered. Then, very nervously indeed, he slowly turned to look at Old School.

As calm as anything Old School said, "Well Franky if I don't get my money you'll end up in this boot next, and you'll be shown off to the next fella that thinks he can get away with my money".

It had shit the life out of me, let alone them. I'd never seen a dead body that close up just yet and by the looks of things they hadn't either.

Frank had turned into a little boy again. "Sorry Old School," he pleaded. "Please mate, it'll be here. You know it will."

"I know it will, Frank. Just making sure its all 50's that's all."

"I'm your friend. I won't let you down Old School, me old mate."

As he slammed the boot shut, Old School continued, "You never can tell with friends, Frank. Hey they're all friends when you're risking your liberty trying to give them the stuff but when you want your money back they're nowhere to be seen or they seem to be in the clubs sniffing it or drinking. When it really comes to the crunch and you're banged up in Her Majesty's hotel they deny they even knew you let alone have got your money for you".

Frank and the minder got in to their Maserati and sped off from the club to get Frank his money to pay Old School.

Old School and me left Epping Forest a bit sharpish, as you would if you had a dead man in the boot of your motor as you didn't need to get stopped by the Old Bill like that. It was far away from Halloween when maybe you 'd have had half a chance if the police caught you. You couldn't really say it was just a little joke to scare your little brother with, could ya? A joke Frank didn't find funny, but he managed to pay Old School back all in 50'es. But like all money it comes in and goes straight out again to the next fella that you owe it to. If you stopped sniffing then maybe a few quid would actually be made. The only thing is it's hard to hide money, especially when you have bundles of it. A few do, maybe more than some of the richest men in London. It's just they don't make a show of it or let on or know the right money launderers so it can be hidden or shipped out to other countries, or be invested with the right people. When you're in the know you're in the know.

Falling behind with the work for Mr B and the plan for the shooting in London

Now Mr B knew I was getting Peru's favourite flake, the finest, and like everyone he wanted a piece of the pie himself so he wanted to sort out some true villains and pay back some favours that were owed with what we could get. So a little deal was now arranged for some to be picked up. I had to meet up with Mr B out in the country in the back of an old gun shop where the money had been stashed by the main villains of the underworld.

We sat down and counted out two lots of £29,000. It wasn't easy counting out all the notes especially when most were in £10 notes and the dreaded £5 notes. It took a long time putting the notes in order and the Queen's head all facing each other and putting elastic bands round each £1000. Doing it by hand took us ages, nearly a whole day, and I never thought you could be sick of counting money, but you try counting that much! All this had to be done so we could pick up this merchandise from a top firm that was exporting large amounts of cocaine.

Old School had good connections with this firm. He'd worked with them over in Spain, Morocco and other places. He promised that this would be the crème de la crème of gear that we were picking up, and that I'd only make an eighth of the gear for now. Fair enough. We could earn

£3000 each for our troubles on the second. I said it needed to be the crème de la crème as the people we were getting it for didn't mess around, and were the crème de la crème of people, the true villains of the underworld. Old School gave me his word and it was arranged, but I don't think he believed me about who we might have been getting this gear for, not until it all came crashing down on him, well really on us both.

On the way up to pick this parcel up we phoned Mr B and told him we were off to stay in Florida and if he needed us we would be in Disneyland. We were joking of course, now we had his money on board which he wasn't too happy about. I can't blame him. So we headed to pick this little lot up which was up to Dover. But before we set off we needed to get a photo of the lorry we had to get the stuff from. So a little detour was made as we went on the search for this little pub, to meet up with someone that was in the know about the lorry and people we had to meet up with.

Before long me and Old School went in to this small local Irish pub which was in Oxford Street London, so we could get this photo. We knew who we were working with cos you never know what the police might have come up with. It could have been a set up for all we knew. It's been done before, this sort of entrapment. That's why these things were done the way they were with the photo and all that. Some times it was like being a secret agent with some of the things that went on and still do today, no doubt.

As we walked into this Irish pub, everyone in there stopped doing what they were doing and turned around. Instead of a big warm welcome it was instant silence and all eyes were heading in our direction and it felt well uncomfortable. AFTER ALL WE WERE IN SOME ONE ELSE'S PUB AND MANOR, and I knew if we'd come in for a drink we would have left through the locals trying to throw us out with the rubbish or having a fight. Then a middle aged Irish man came to save the day. He shouted out "No worries fella's. These are my boys." After that the pub erupted in small talk again. We were led to a table where Old School was given an envelope by this Irish fella. In it was a photo and on the back were some numbers and letters. "Can you do this?" the fella said "because you can take a horse to the water but you can't get him to drink."

"I can do this" Old School replied. "This is the start of many more, my friend."

"Well, top of the morning to you, son." They both laughed.

When we were back in the car I asked Old School what the numbers were. He said they were the car number plate numbers. This is the car that wanted the money. Old School flicked the photo around and said "That's the Spanish lorry we need to park next to." It was a big arterial lorry with the Spanish flag stamped down the side of it.

Now this deal would have been regular as clockwork every few months if Old School hadn't fucked it all up before we even began. We had just arranged a meeting with Old School's top firm members. Now what Old School hadn't told me was that the firm he was working for was, yes, a top firm. It didn't bother me as I'd worked for a well known one myself which he had no idea of at the time and I'd never let on to.

Old School was behind in paying them off. They were sick of him owing them money and wanted ways to get their money back from him anyhow they could get it even if it meant keeping the money that wasn't his and putting the debt on Old School's head. He thought this was something they wouldn't do. After all, he was making them a lot of dough and a lot of contacts for them. Even though he'd fallen behind he thought they wouldn't do that to him as it was well out of the character of this firm. But money's money at the end of the day no matter where it comes from or who and if you owe it you're always in their pockets and obliged to do them all sorts of little favours. Whether you liked it or not, they controlled your life for you, really. Well, you owed it, not them, and it's hard to walk away when you owe so much money or money you might never see in this life time.

All this was unknown to me, as we thought Old School had made it. I thought we were back in for the big timers again but if the truth be known I was just trying to help Mr B out, and yes, OK, make a few quid along the way for myself, a little nest egg but not ripping any one off. Far from it. Some people have some morals. I was just blinded by all what was going on in front of me. My first ever big dangerous deal left me excited until it went sour, very sour indeed. After this one I vowed I'd stop doing the risky work and arrange for it to be picked up and delivered. I'd earn three large on the next job without even being there or making any calls. Just being paid. Sometimes you have to speculate to accumulate and put yourself on offer or that was my thinking for now anyhow.

I could do this first job and just take a loss for now and collect my wages on the next bit of big work that they wanted. After all we're not in this game for nothing and we don't do it for love so to make £1000 grand on the next one seemed only fair enough to me. After all that was a small amount compared to what they'd make and I was risking my life in the booth again by driving it back.

Well we got there me and Old School. We drove slowly down into the docks. It was a nice sunny day and it was pleasantly warm. We pulled in next to a big Spanish arterial lorry. Old School looked at the photo to make sure it was the correct truck and that the number plate of the awaiting car matched the one drawn on the back of this photo. He then opened the boot of the car and handed the big bags of money to the car waiting next to this lorry. It was a convertible Bently with blacked out windows. Two men were leaning by the doors with hands down their side and clasped in front of them. They looked like body guards. Well, for all I knew they were. They definitely looked the part. They were both big men dressed in black suits looking like the fellas out of the Men in Black with shades on and ear pieces in their ears. They spoke in Spanish. There was a old man in the back of the car sitting on the edge of the back seat just looking at me and Old School. He looked a bit like Ronnie Biggs and might well have been as Ronnie had just escaped from prison and was heading out to Spain.

Well, the bags of cash were handed over to one of the fellas. He put them into the boot of his car, then opened them and pulled out a pen. He lifted the first bundles up and put the pen across the notes, then smiled as it was one of those fake detector pens. He pulled a bundle, handed it to the Ronnie Biggs look-a-like and got in the car. The other man got in and they drove off, leaving us standing next to the lorry, the one in the photo. Then the driver of the lorry took the two kilos of powder off his truck and put it into our awaiting car. Me and Old School headed back as you wouldn't want to be sitting around with about ten years in your boot and as we had Old School's word there was no need to stop off and sniff or wash it up to see what it was all about.

What we didn't know was that they had given Old School repressed gear, not what he'd promised me and I'd promised Mr B. It weren't what Old School had shown me before when we were in his manor with a few girls and bouncers that we'd brought back from the Epouram night club one night when we were all sniffed up and there were large amounts spread all over the glass table for us to help ourselves to. It seemed everywhere I went I just couldn't get away from the sniff and the people that went with it, and by sniffing myself I couldn't see a way out. But I wasn't helping matters and by getting more involved I was well and truly in the thick of things.

We got back to Mr B. I couldn't wait to hand the stuff over and get the respect I was looking for as I knew he always looked on me as his little boy. But I was no boy now. I was there with the boys doing what they did but the thing was I was only playing at it. These were true players of this game and they knew the circus well, They'd all been there for sometime and pulled through it so why couldn't I? When the crunch came Old School had chipped off back to his manor and left me to face the music which he also was unaware of.

"What the fuck is this? It's fucking bollocks. Where did you get this from?"

It was something I couldn't divulge as it was more than my life's worth or my families. Well, I was in a big mess. I needed to get this money back and where the fuck could I get it? Yes, I was sick. I knew a few bank robbers who'd hand over their money to me after they'd risked their liberty but how could I pay it back? It's OK borrowing but what about paying back? The only way would be to go on the job with them myself. I did eye up a few security vans as there'd been a little job done in South Mimms where a cash machine was nicked by a forklift, but that wouldn't have enough for me to sort this debt out, far from it.

Mr B and Old School met for a brief moment before we went to get these fines which turned out to be the worst bit of powder we'd ever seen .It was so bad it might as well have been baby powder. Mr B said it could be worked but it was only about 25 percent and if you mixed it to sell it in the streets it would only be about 10 percent, no good to man or beast and no good for a man like Mr B. He wanted his money there and then. Well, you couldn't blame him. It's a lot of money to lose. "I don't care how you get it" Mr B told Old School, "even if you have to sell your arse in Kings Cross or even risk selling the shit I want my money. In fact, Old School, you're going to tell me where you got it from."

"I can't. Leave it with me. I'll get it back for you."

"You'd best do that, lad, otherwise you'll be pushing up the daisies, dead money or no money, as now there's two of you in this mess and if I kill you." (He was pointing at me.) "He can sort my money out."

We were well in trouble and well out of our depths. There were too many of them to go round shooting them all. Old School left and tried to go on the run to bide a little time to see what to do next with one of the parcels. Mr B got everyone in his firm together to bring Old School to him. When they got him, they put a rat on his chest and a bucket over it and set fire to the bucket. When the rat started clawing at him the info came out about how they could get to see the other firm members. That's after they'd beaten him to a pulp until he spilled the beans on where they could get in touch with this firm.

Now they had the info they could get the money back. That's after Old School had tried to sell some of this shit before Mr B came and got him. After some time and a great deal of putting feelers out, Mr B met up in Mexico with the family firm and the Spanish connection. The family firm gave the money to Mr B's firm without no dramas but it was less than 25 grand as they'd put that on Old School's head. Only fair, after all, he'd fucked up the deal and did owe them this money.

So it was all sorted. Mr B wasn't happy but had to wipe his mouth with this firm as now they'd met they could do a roaring trade between them and make much more money than 25 grand. Looking back, Mr. B did very well meeting this firm as he'd never be introduced to them any other way. They were a proper family firm and are well connected all over the world. They had their fingers in all the pies and scams that were going on. They even had connections with the Old Bill and terrorists.

So £25000 had been put on Old School's and my head we had to pay back this money. Shit! With this on my mind I couldn't think straight and started just giving up. I gave all I could to Mr B to try pay him back. I sold my cars, I borrowed ten grand from the bank, I called in all my tickers, but I was just falling behind with other debts and sniffing. With all this on my mind, it drove me mad. We were falling more behind, as we weren't able to pay the heavies as now they were putting interest on the money owed. We had no chance, so me and Old School drove to Somerset to see his girl friend and try get away from it all for a little while and hide from the heavies for now.

On the way back we ticked some more cocaine off someone Old School knew. He didn't care any more and neither did I. We just wanted to sniff ourselves into oblivion and get off our heads, a sort of escape for now. What we should have done is pulled ourselves together and come up with a plan on how to get the money back and stop eating E's like they were Smarties and sniffing cocaine as if our life depended on it. Well, it did for now. On the way back from Somerset we sniffed all day and night. When I got home to K's I sniffed in my Car as I couldn't bear being in her house paranoid to the max. I just kept sniffing and trying to eat the cocaine from the wraps the cocaine had been put in.

All I had to do was stop sniffing, but you try it when one line has all ready passed your nose and a thousand more have followed. The cloud of impending doom had shown up again and with the paranoia showing me the shadows and the Grim Reaper standing by my side touching me, I couldn't take any more. I was a broken man. At that point my whole illusion had been shattered. There was nothing really important about trying to please Mr B, the clubs or about the flash cars, the women, being Charley Big Bollocks, the hotels, or the feeling important. It had to end somewhere, and for me there was no way out of the circus let alone any room for more jugglers like Old School. He'd just made the circus that bit bigger.

All of a sudden a police car came over the hill and noticed me looking round and mumbling to myself in a non-coherent state. The officer got out and pulled his truncheon out and tried to pull me to the floor but without success, as I wasn't aware of what was really going on. Talk about kick a man when he's down but he was just doing his job. Then loads of police turned up and led me to the waiting van and before long I was standing in front of the judges. I had come down from the cocaine frenzy and was now looking at seven years trying to explain why I had a pocket full of narcotics. "What can I say? Wow your honour, they weren't there when I left home."

I had been caught, and rightly so, in my state of unawareness and with loads of narcotics all wrapped up in my pockets my future looked dim. The best place for me was prison but no one likes to admit it and I still owed this debt that Old School had put on my head from our messed up deal. He'd told me he would make us a few quid. Yeah right, probably the biggest liberty taker I've ever met so far, and there's many out there. So I arrived in Wood Hill. This would be my new home for the next few months before I got shipped out to Pentonville where I would stay for nine months and where I'd earn the name the Caveman as I'd live like one in there as people who knew me will tell ya.

I could tell you loads about what a nasty place prison can be but I'll keep it small, and straight to the point. Get there, get training in the gym, get your head straight and get out and if you're lucky learn some thing. I met up with Mr Adams in Pentonville, a proper gentleman, a very moral man and respected throughout the prison system and by the people who knew him. People went out their way to help with little perks here and there which are well needed in a place like that, and I appreciated them for it, giving it to us even if I hadn't shown it at times. We were banged up in Pentonville together and he made my stay there as pleasant as possible, as he had the nick sewn right up.

We were living it large or as large as could be in there, even though it wasn't a very nice place to be. He even had the prison guards working for him, bringing in cigarettes and booze etc. That's when we got talking and I told him about the debt I was in one night after a chess game. We'd play for hours at a time just to pass the time away, and he told me how I was going to sort it. It all sounded great but I'd heard it all before from loads of people but as luck would have it he delivered the goods.

When it was exercise in the prison regime that meant

all us prisoners were allowed out for one hour in the yard to walk about, do all their wheeling and dealing, get messages passed and other bits and bobs before we were banged up again behind doors. Mr Adams walked over to this fella who was a proper face and well respected in the underworld. He had a few faces around him and even though they were all doing long times for various crimes themselves they were still pulling strings on the outside. Their crimes ranged from bank jobs to shootings, robbery, smuggling, disposing of bodies, money laundering and fraud and not forgetting demanding money with menace.

I was introduced to a man who had more than enough money to pay my debts off as I found out later on. He had been in prison for stealing a million pounds worth of diamonds from a Swedish jewellers and of course the diamonds never turned up again even though he was caught. He 'd done many jobs or been behind many jobs and only been caught for this one. He was the mastermind for nearly half the jobs going on around London at the time or that's what other crooks said. Whether true or not they also said he'd worked for the notorious Krays now and then. Also it was said he has many different connections with the mafi. Who knows? Talk was cheap. I'd learnt that. It turned out that someone on the outside had done him a right wronging and bubbled everyone up who were involved in the robbery.

I got talking to the fella who it turned out knew Wong from Chinatown. I didn't let on that I knew him as well as no one really needed to know who I knew or didn't. I liked it that way too. I was no one really so the least I knew the better. What I needed to know was what I knew. That's how I liked it and that's how it stayed.

Well, this inmate told me that Wong knew where this no good fella was and had been keeping a eye on him for almost a year now, getting all the info like where he worked, lived, drank etc etc.. Wong knew his mate inside, who was now on the back end of ten years would soon need to know where this fella was. Someone had been shot on his job and because of this fella the gang that done it were now all banged up, apart from their supposed friend who was a gang member who'd turned grass and thought the grass was greener on the other side by bubbling them. That's where I came into it, to show him it wasn't by choice but I was in a hole and needed a way out.

So this fella in the prison yard said "Son, listen, Mr Adams has told me your proper stuff and he's been keeping an eye on you and your family, and he told me that you've got problems on the outside, don't mind do ya"? He said a small matter of some debts, well to them it was small, but to me it was a big problem and was hanging over my head like a black cloud. How was I to get this money now, stuck in prison? It wouldn't be long before Mr B's Minders or debt collectors, one who was called the governor, were kicking down my mum's door demanding payment by menacing. I'd seen them do it in the old days, with me being there to watch and oversee it. Now the tables had turned I could be on the receiving end of it for my own debts. "Mr Adams is very particular who he makes his friends or acquaintances" this fella said to me in his deep husky voice. "So, son", the fella said "when you get out if you'd do me a little favour then you'll have no more debt to ever worry about." I'd heard this all before, promises and small talk, but I had no choice but to believe in him. What else did I have? Only this fella and his word to get me out this mess Old School had left me with. And he'd would see me right, and I'd be well looked after.

After over several weeks of meeting in the prison yard

with the fella he came up with a little plan on how to get this gang member who'd turned grass, and who was out and about without a care in the world thinking that these people wouldn't be getting out. That's what people think once you go into prison. They don't think they'll see you again, like it's a big vortex or something. Well, it weren't far off. Life moves fast on the out side and slow on the inside but at least you get time to think in there with the rats and cockroaches. Well, the world's a big place but when you mix in these circles the world can be a very small one indeed. If only he knew what was being plotted against him, this guy, I'm sure he wouldn't have been smiling in the clubs and thinking he'd got away with bubbling gang members up saying he'd had a close one and had been let off. He even believed he'd got off it himself by the things he was doing, going in to all these old hornets.

The plan was this fella needed to be sorted and he was going to get it. A contract had been put out on this fella's head of 30 grand. It had been shown to me first, and the word was to go out on the street amongst other crimes two weeks after I'd leave the nick so I'd have time to do it. Just enough to see me right. Not bad? It's weird you don't always think straight when you see the money and go over and over it in your head. It sometimes can warp your mind for that split instance and you can even touch all the crisp fifty pound notes with the Queen all dressed up and looking her best on each one even before you've got them.

This would mean no more worries. My family would be safe and able to sleep at night. I could walk away from the circus. Before you know it you're doing the job that the money is warranted for and you now find yourself sitting on the back of a motor bike with a colt 45 stuck through a hole in your leathers driving through Covent

Garden with a photo of the person you have to shoot on the back of the bike drivers back. You're ready to let the trigger go and let this fella have it and collect your money.

Leaving prison and the porridge days behind with a shooting in London

So the time did eventually come round to me leave the maddest place on earth. I ate my last bowl of prison porridge. The prisons old wife's tale is that if you eat your porridge you won't come back. True or false I'm yet to find out. So I sat down and had my last bowl with the two most decent people I could ever have done my bird with at Springhill. One was my training partner Steve who is still there and the other fella we'll nickname the Money Launderer.

Now I know why they call it doing time cos you've got so much of it doing nothing, just lying on your bed counting the hours. You're actually waiting for the time to pass instead of it passing you by like it does on the outside where things move faster and without you knowing it, not at half pace as it did in there when you're looking at the cell walls. I left Springhill with three things, my sanity, a book full of contacts and the knowledge of all the other ways that criminals do things. That's why some people come out worse than when they went in or more criminal minded at least.

I walked out the prison gates and a big weight was taken off my shoulders. All the frustration had passed and I was a free man once again, free from the circus, free from the lock-up of prison, free from the keys turning and the doors slamming shut, and from the bells going off every time there was a fight or someone had hung themselves. Free from the fantasies of the lady prison officers wanting to have sex with you. The light from the sun hurt my eyes as they grew accustomed to the light outside. My eyes had become used to the poorly lit lights in the dirty dingy smelling cells. You seem to adapt well, a voice said in the back of my head. Well you have no choice but to in there, I thought again.

I stepped out a bit more to be greeted by little K. She'd stuck by me in there and still is around today. I jumped into her car and she turned and kissed me on the cheek and nearly hugged me to death. Then she said "Where to?"

I said "The Savoy Hotel, London." This had been planned by Mr Adams' friend, the fellow back at Pentonville, the Swedish jeweller's thief.

"Sorry?" she said, a bit shocked as to where we were going.

I said "Don't worry. It's all cool. I have to meet an old friend there."

"That's all OK."

"And stay the night or maybe a few." K was good like that. She never real cared what was going on or made out she wasn't as long as she was happy. We arrived at the hotel and booked in. We were shown to our room and what a room it was, marble everywhere and gold tints with a four poster bed that was going to see a lot of action as I hadn't been with a woman for two years and I felt like a virgin again, but that soon changed after a nice meal! I'd been inside for enough time that when the butler was standing there for his tips after bringing up our bags I forgot all about tipping him. You forget that's what happens to people who have done years and years. I shook his hand instead and he stayed there. I walked in to the bathroom and when I came out he was still there. I said "K, what's he still here for?" She laughed and gave him £50 and said thanks.

When he went me K both laughed. I showered and walked out on to the balcony with a glass of champagne and a few strawberries that had been bought to our room. Not bad, I thought, for someone who'd just left prison. I looked out over London and went over in my head what I was doing here, what I'd been told in prison, what I'd learned from some of the good people I'd met and also what I had to do. As I was thinking K asked what I was doing here and how could we afford it. "Don't worry, sweetheart" I said. "I've met some nice people in there", not wanting her to know anything untowards. She didn't need to know, only enjoy the place as it's not every day you get to be in the Savoy. Well, not just after leaving prison, hey?.

It weren't long before a call came through to our room and I was asked to go to the foyer. I went down and left K smoking a joint on the bed watching a film in the nice room.

It was Wong. "Hi son, good to see you. You don't look so bad. We'll have you back to form in no time at all." He was acting as if he'd known me for years even though I'd only seen him with Sam that night when we went to his restaurant and a few times afterwards when I'd done a few deals with him. Each time he'd come across quite hostile, but right now he was, or seemed to be my best friend, or it seemed like I was the best thing since sliced bread. That's how it seemed as we walked out of the hotel lobby. His Bentley was parked ready waiting for us with its own driver to take me to get some clobber as the fellow in prison had arranged. I'd heard so much in prison and been promised so much by different people, but now it was really happening.

The Bentley slowly pulled out from the Savoy's long entrance and we headed to an Italian shop in Oxford Street that Wong knew well and had done regular business with. I would be kitted out with some top clobber and a fine expensive Armani suit, which had been made to measure. While I was there Wong had my name embroidered in the back of the jacket The label read 'Cookster, Welcome to the Family' in small gold letters. Wong said, "You need a good decent suit, son, and some shoes for when the man himself comes out of prison, which will be pretty soon if he gets parole... and we'd best get you a proper decent watch, as a watch and shoes can tell what sort of man you are or may be.'

I laughed "Morals and standards tell what sort of a man you are."

Wong smiled, "You're learning, boy."

So next it was to go and get me a two grand Cartier watch, all paid for by the Swedish jewel thieves that were still in prison, and then some Italian shoes and some other casual clobber just for now. When me, Wong and the driver of the Bentley arrived at the Savoy. Wong asked the driver to pass him over a big fat brown envelope which he then passed to me. As I got out of the car and thanked him, he said "Don't thank me, son. Thank him when he comes out the nick as he's sorted this all out for you, not me." We said goodbye and he said, "I won't see you now until the deed is done. OK, boy?"

I said "Goodbye fellows" and walked into the Savoy concealing the fat envelope under my long moleskin trench coat that I'd had bought for me. I looked in the glass mirror and thought I looked like the Million Dollar Man far from the Caveman or two bob I'd once looked like or been nicknamed in prison. If the boys could see me now, I thought.

The doors opened and closed again. No one came into the lift so I pulled the envelope free and tore at the top end carefully and looked in. Wow! I then left the lift and concealed it under my arm again. Inside was £3000 in crisp new 50 notes with a piece of paper wrapped around it. On the paper it said 'Use the money but spend wisely'. There was a number to phone and a place where the phone box would be that I had to use. GO TO THE PHONE BOX IN LEICESTER SQUARE, THE ONE WHERE IF YOU PICK UP THE PHONE YOU CAN SEE THE MC DONALD'S WITHOUT TURNING ROUND. SAY YOUR NICKNAME, THE WORD CAVEMAN, AND LISTEN TO THE FELLA AND WHAT TO DO OR WHERE TO MEET NEXT. DO NOT USE YOUR PHONE.' So I put the note into my pocket and went into the room and said "Come on, K. Let's go get some thing to eat."

"But we have no more money" she replied.

"Don't worry. We do now sweetheart" I showed her the £3000.

"What have you done? Who have you robbed?"

"No one, ha. Come, K, trust me.

"OK lets eat", she said so off we went with no more questions from her. I said there were a few nice restaurants in Leicester Square. So we went to look for one in Leicester Square and for me to find this phone box without her twigging what was really going on. We took a black cab to the Square. As we drew into the Square I looked around until I could see the right phone box which the note had told me to look out for.

There it was. The phone box was at the east side but if I picked up the phone I'd need to turn round to see the McDonalds ads. I said "K, let's go in here and have a little drink." So we sat down in a little bar watching people walk past. It was night time by now and there were people all over the Square. I said I needed the toilet so I walked round the back of the wine bar towards the toilet and then slipped out the door unseen by K. I looked around me and headed towards the phone box, put 1 pound in, looked around again and pulled the note out my pocket to phone the number. Ring! The phone was picked up but with no greeting. "Hello". It was dead "Hello, it's me."

"Who?" said a real deep gangster's voice.

"The Caveman."

"Don't speak, just listen. I can see you but you can't see me."

"So what now?" I said

"Someone will send a car in the morning for yah at the hotel."

Then the line went dead before I could say much more. It got me thinking he could see me and I couldn't see him so was I being followed. Of course I was! I headed back to K in the wine bar, sat down and forgot all about the call instantly. We then headed for a club and got drunk and danced the night away together. Some people at the club were pleased to see that I was out and came over to join us and congratulate me on being out, and asked if I needed anything. The night came to an end and we got back to the Savoy at about 4.30 in the morning. We made love and fell asleep.

Ring! "Hi sir, there's a car down here for you."

"Thanks" I said. I slipped out of bed carefully leaving K still sleeping, got in to the shower, dressed and went down. There outside was a black taxi. I got in and it drove off with out me saying where to. All through the journey the driver didn't even speak to me. He just looked at me now and then in the mirror.

We arrived outside the Bank of England and the driver slid open his window and handed me another envelope "Here, cocker. I was told to give you this and wait here."

I said "yeah?"

He said "Yeah." I tore open the envelope and in it was a note 'Go into the bank. Show them the key and ask them to phone this number." I did this and before long I was taken to the safety boxes. I opened the box and in it was £30,000 in cash and a map of Watford with a pub circled in it, a phone number coming off it and two brand new bullets. Well, I knew why I was there and it wasn't for the money just yet as I hadn't done the job yet so the money wasn't mine. I took the bullets out and the map and put the cash back in. I was tempted to take it now, though, but I locked the box and walked outside the vault.

The fellow that had shown me in said "Are you happy, sir?"

"Yes" I said. I jumped back in to the taxi and went back to the hotel, keeping the map and the bullets out of the way and on me at all times. K and me arrived home and things were pretty much the same as when I went away only this time my drugs problem wasn't anywhere near what it was like when I went in. In fact I hadn't done none for some time. I'd just continued to train and stay on track.

A day later it was time to go to Watford and get this job done for the Swedish jeweller thieves just as I had said I would in prison. Then the money in the box would be mine and the circus would be finished. Mr B would be paid and I could walk free from all the madness and live a normal life. It was about half eight at night that I'd gone over to Watford and rang the number on the map I'd got out the box. Also there was a deadline date on the back of it which I hadn't seen until now and it was the date the Swedish jeweller had or would be released so now that meant I had two days to go to sort this little errand out before he'd be out himself and maybe do it himself. I phoned the number and the same voice came the day I rang in London from the phone box in Leicester Square. "Hi it's me, the Caveman."

"I've been waiting for you to ring", came the deep thick gangster's voice, "Did you take what was there?"

Not wanting him to know I said, "I took what I needed to."

"Ok then you need what I have here. Stay where you are and I'll send another car to you."

Within five minutes a Merc pulled up to me, and a man in the front called me over "Hi son, get in."

The fellow in the back had on a baseball cap just above his eyes and a polo neck pulled up above his mouth and resting on his nose. I got in and the fellow in the back looked out the window and handed me a Mac Donald's bag, "Here, son. This is for you" he mumbled underneath his polo neck.

"I'm not hungry."

"Well you'll have trouble eating this. It's far from a Big Mac mate". I opened the bag and felt a bit stupid. There it was, a shooter. I should have felt the cold steel through the bag. He then drove up to Walthamstow and we pulled up outside a petrol station. As the driver was putting petrol in the car a woman jogger came running past the car window and threw a photo into the car. The man then handed the photo to me. I looked down and saw a man of about 40. Then the driver drove us to an old garage where there was a motorbike which had been stolen the night before. "Son, you stay here now till the morning. Till someone comes in the morning to drive the bike. So get your nut down and do what you've got to do."

I took a deep breath and said, "OK" then made up a bed after looking at the bike. The morning came round and someone was kicking the garage door which woke me up. I hid the gun and the bullets. "Open up, it's me!" I'd heard the voice before but couldn't get the face. It was Old School. "Hi, well I guess we'd best get ready hey, we've got some work to do." I felt better that it was Old School but inside I was still scared and angry at him getting me into this mess. Old School brought in the motorbike leathers and the helmets, and got the bike started. I pulled out the gun and checked that the bullets fitted. As if they wouldn't. They fitted like a glove. I felt sick. Could I do this? What now? Could I walk, just walk away? I knew too much. They'd kill me as I would be a liability by now or worse one of my family could get it.

I put the gun down, wiped the prints off, and pushed the bullets back into the gun with the gloves on. I cut a hole in the leathers so it was easier for me to get the gun out as we'd be driving along when I pulled the trigger. I slid the motorbike lid on and pulled the garage open. I jumped on the back of the bike and vroom! we were off with a little wheel spin wavering in and out of the traffic, heading like a missile to war.

The target was there. There was no messing about. Old School had definitely been briefed about this job. He'd clued me up where the person in the photo would be and how it would work. We'd head to Covent Garden where the fellow I had to shoot would be having tea. We pulled up on the bike. I put my hand in between me and Old School, pulled the gun out of the leathers and pulled the trigger slowly. BANG! Vim! Vroom! We were gone with a wheelie and a scream of the engine and screech of the tyres. The bullet had missed and hit the side of a wall, thank God. Every one screamed and people were diving around all over the gaff. My heart sank.

We ended up in a scrap yard. The gun was put in the crusher and the bike was crushed with the gun. The leathers and helmet were put in the incinerator. We got into a waiting car and headed back the way we'd come. The police had cordoned everywhere off and were everywhere. You couldn't get into the area we'd just left about half hour ago. "Well done son. We're debtless", said Old School. How did he know, I asked. He said he'd been told that if he drove the bike he wouldn't have to worry about the debt owed to Mr B's firm but his debts still stood with the other firms. This was sort of a little favour for them.

I said "I'll get the train home from here." I felt like I was in the middle of a big conspiracy. I felt sick and ashamed and shaken and I didn't trust anyone. Why had I done this? It went round and round in my head. I was no gangster. I didn't think I was on top of the world or Big Potatoes. I was a mess. I got back to Camden and found a bar, got drunk on the docks and went to an old friend's in my drunken state, trying to drown how I really felt inside. I fell asleep on my friend's sofa. In the morning I woke up to my pal's wife cooking breakfast. Feeling a little better I said "Cheers for letting me stay."

"No problems. You're welcome here any time, you know that." I washed, ate and left. I waited for the train to get back home, got on the train and sat down. A lady was reading a paper in front of me. I looked up and there it was in black and white, MAN SHOT DEAD IN COVENT GARDEN. The train came to a halt and she put the paper down and left. I snatched up the paper and read the article. It was the same man I'd tried to get but he was found dead outside his house. Someone had shot him in the back of the head. They said it must have been a mercenary or hit man who'd done it. So now I was in trouble surely. They would know I hadn't done it.

My mobile went. It was the Swedish fella from the nick. "Hi son, I'm out. Well done! I've heard the news so the box is yours", meaning the security box with the £30,000.

"Yes" I said.

"I'll meet you at the back of the History night club tonight. It's my welcoming do. Wear your suit with your name in the back that we had done for you and don't worry son, it gets better from here on."

"Yes" I said. The phone went dead. What a relief I hadn't done it. Someone had though, so who? But if they thought I'd done it then that was cool. I could take a gamble, take the money and pay Mr B and walk away from the circus.

The night time came and I dressed up in the Armani suit that had been made for me by this firm ready for the welcoming party for the man himself the main Swedish jeweller thief or the man with the brains behind it. On the day this jeweller theif had come out he'd also sorted out a security Bobby over in heathrow by the robbers he shared cells with. They'd robbed the van and would also be meeting up at the little do behind the Astoria so they could count all the money out. Now they were million-aires.

I arrived, was frisked and walked in. I was given a drink, on the house, of course. I sat down and everyone welcomed me with respect as I was the man who'd cleaned up their little mess for them or so they thought. It was better than having the fellow turn grass if they turned up in court. Alian Champs and whisky and endless Jack Daniel's were being drunk. Faces known and unknown were everywhere, all villains. The raiders of the security van came in with the case of money and it was all tipped out on the table. There were bundles of notes all in plastic bags. There were 25 bags and each one must have contained £500,000 grand in 50's, 10's and 5's. Not bad for just some one getting out of prison and meeting the correct people whilst serving time. The money was all counted. No one would nick any cos most of them were all self made millionaires themselves and had seen money like this many times.

The partying went on for the rest of the night. I was treated like the hero of the place. It was said all this couldn't have been possible if I hadn't got this fella for them. I was leaning by the bar looking suave in my new suit when this good looking lady came over. "So you're the fella they're all talking about then? Hey!"

"Who are you?" I said.

"I'm Mandy."

"Well, Mandy, sweetheart, don't believe everything you hear."

"I don't" she replied. "Actions speak louder than words to me. I hear you're a wealthy man."

Now that's what all the nice women tell me. It's amazing what they'll tell ya if they think you have a few quid. I'm not what you think sweet heart, I said to myself. No. "Now Mandy, I'm like Dire Straits darling."

Ya?" she said "How's that, then?"

I replied "I like my money for nothing and my chicks for free. I'm far from what you may have heard."

She said "Don't worry I'm not here for the money. I'm here cos I was invited." Who by, I thought? "Listen, I've been there, seen it, and done it and worn

the tee shirt and its not very nice sweetheart, believe me. I'm far from being or pretending to be one of these fella's or face or gangsters. It's just not me. They're in a different class."

She said "I like honesty in a man. You're kind of cute."

I could feel some movement in the trouser department. Now that's honesty, I thought. She was nice, very cunning and had the best figure in the party and every other man's eyes were on her but right now she was with me for some reason. "Can I get you a drink" I said.

"Why don't you grab a bottle and come with me?" she replied.

"So your house or mine?" I replied. "With all the men in this club and you had to come over to me. Why?"

"You're kind of cute."

"Ha" I laughed.

"And you seem a bit different from some of them. They're all full of it".

"You're not bad yourself, sweetheart" I replied. "So why don't we get to know each other better then?" Now that the Jack D's were in full swing I felt a bit confident and the lines were rolling of my tongue and not up my nose for once. Just what I'd in mind. We left after everyone had thanked me for being there and £5000 was handed to me before we left. It was a little token from the robbery and a little thank you from the Swedish jeweller thieves or that's what they said. I've never seen or been to a party like it again. It was proper out of this world and you had to see it to believe it.

I arrived with this Mandy girl at her house. We walked in and started kissing. Hands were all over the place caressing each other. "Stop" she said. "I know all about you".

I said "I hope it's all good things as I'm not proud of the bad."

She said "I know more than what you think. I'm not just your average blonde, you know".

So I said "Let me guess. You're some gangster's moll and when he finds out I'm with you he's going to kill me if he knows we've been having a bit of fun?"

"You're not far wrong" she said.

"Ha" I laughed, giving it a bit of large.

She led me to the sofa and poured me a drink. She then let down her hair and put red lipstick on in a seductive way then pulled up her skirt flashing her stocking tops. She then got on her hands and knees and curled over to me flashing her cleavage. Wow, if the boys could see me now, I thought. She came right over to me, put her hands on my belt and said "I'm going to give you some oral, yeah."

I thought, crack on, sitting up a bit and opening my legs more.

"Yeah" she said, pulling down my trousers and pants at the same time. She put her lips on my piece and then stood up. What was going on, I thought. OK, a little tease, no problem. She then pulled her clothes together.

"I thought you were going to give me some oral" I said.

She laughed "OK, ready for it big boy"?

"Oh yes, darling" I said.

"Here goes then. Get ready for it. Here goes! I do know you didn't kill that man, you know."

"What!" I said.

"I bet that's the best bit of oral you've ever had" she said, as she winked at me. Shit! If she knew, who else knew, I thought. I'd been set up. I sobered up instantly, pulled up my trousers, a bit embarrassed by now. My heart was beating fast. " Didn't I?" I replied.

She said "Shush" as she leant forward pushing her finger on to my lips and then slowly kissing them. "I know you never" she whispered in my ear.

"Who did then?" I said out loud, moving away from her. "Do you know"?

"I don't but I want you to meet someone who does." She took the drink out of my hand and led me to the door. We walked out of her house and out of her gate. At the same time a nice new black Land Rover pulled up. As if this wasn't planned I thought. I had been well and truly set up.

The Land Rover pulled up just outside her house. "Get in son" said a deep voice. "I'm Mandy's brother son". He was a man of few words but the few words he did say spoke volumes to me. Looking at him he could have passed for Vinny Jones I thought. They looked so similar and he had the same sort of mannerisms that Vinny had.

I had the pleasure to meet Vinny whilst in the Pentonville prison's gym when he'd come to do some filming of his new film at the time. He was one right nice fella. He had time for everyone, and definitely looked the part. Money hadn't changed him. Whilst we were there together in Pentonville, me and Vinny had a few personal chats about old and new times and about the people we knew or had met along our way. We played some football in the prison gym too which was good. Vinny said "Cookster, I'd like to give you something before I go. Take this" he said as he

152

pulled off his number ten shirt that he wore in the film The Mean Machine and he signed it personally to me. His other pal did the same and gave the other signed shirt to one of the other prisoners, He'd been in Lock Stock and Two Smoking Barrels. He too was a proper face and a right funny fella. Vinny gave me a firm handshake before he left to which I replied, "it's been a pleasure". On leaving the prison to go to a new one the shirt mysteriously disappeared from my property. The story might have been that some prison guard had stolen it for all we knew as it went mysteriously missing from a high security building. For all I know it's now on a prison guard's back when he's playing Sunday league somewhere or on Mr T's wall. Thieves amongst Thieves, hey!

"Get in son" came the Vinny Jones villain's voice. So I got in. We then drove off slowly away from the house. "Do you like my little sister, then, son"?

"She's far from little. She's about 32" I said.

"Do yourself a little favour. Stay away from her. She may not be little but she's still my sister. This will be the last time you see or hear from her. Think of your little meeting as a wet dream, son, if you know what's best for you." He then said, "I know you didn't kill the fella boy. Didn't I say? Come on, son. I didn't just jump off the boat you know. You're amongst friends here."

"How do you know I didn't do it then, hey?"

He paused then turned and looked at me, pulled the gun from his trousers and said "Cos I did". Shit, now what, I thought. I was right in the lion's den. Then it all came to me. The voice on the telephone in Leicester Square was his. He said, "Son you're a nice fella and son you have something of mine that belongs to me."

"What do I have?"

"The money from the security box. The rest of Mr B's money what you owe him." I handed him the key for the box. He pulled up in a little lane then got out of the Land Rover and told me to come to his boot, after handing me some blue carrier bags. Was this it? I thought he was going to shoot me there and then wrap me in these bags. He opened the boot and there was a case. He opened it up and there was ten grand. He handed it to me and I put it into the bags he'd given me. I noticed that underneath the money he had another shooter. He removed it and closed the case down. "There, son. That's your bit. 10 for me, 10 Mr for B and 10 for you."

"Seems fair considering the circumstances. I'll get mine and Mr B's out the security box when you give me the keys back."

We got back into the Land Rover and he said, "Son, you're a boy playing a man's game". I nodded looking at the gun now sticking out towards my head. As we drove back he asked where I wanted to be dropped off. The woods maybe?"

"No," I said, "the wood. Borehamwood" So we headed there. I got out the car, took the money to my pal's house and put it in his safe. I came back out to him like he said I'd best do and I got back in to the Land Rover. He then drove me to the hilltop where we used to hang out when I was 16, a few acquaintances and me. We pulled up. I looked out at the hill and looked back at it all. This way I'd still made £5000 from the party and just paid my debt back to Mr B and still walked away with no debt, no circus, no dramas. As I went to get out the Land Rover never to see Mandy's brother's face again, he turned to me and said "One more thing son."

"Yea" I said as he put the cold gun into my mouth and lent to whisper to my ear. I tried and say please and beg for my life. My body was limp and nearly ready to shut down. I had let go of all my muscular functions and I could feel wet in my pants and in my eyes. For a minute I wanted to say "Go on then, do it" but he might have done it then. I just sat there with it in my mouth and prayed. All the good times came flooding back one after the other like a picture book being flicked. My eyes welled with water and my mind went blank once more as he leant slowly over to my ear. Pictures of Chelsea and Hughie G flashed before me in my mind. Then he said in a slow cold dead deafening voice "Son …………"

"Yea!" I mumbled.

"THERE'S NO ROOM FOR JUGGLERS IN MY CIRCUS."

It went quiet. It seemed the words went on and on over and over again in my head. He then pulled the trigger and shouted Bang! I waited and it went dark and I could feel my breath slipping away from me. Then he pulled the gun free from my mouth and gave me a little slap on the left cheek to bring me to. I had collapsed. "Well, son" he said.

I nodded.

He then said "I'm Johnny, the hit man. Nice to see ya, to see ya nice," as if nothing had happened. "I'm a friend of Mr Nice and I'm sure you'll read all about him too."

I got out the Land Rover and my jelly legs couldn't hold me up any more. I dropped to my knees and kissed the floor. I felt sick and breathless. Mr Nice laughed, who had been sitting in the back, picked up a large Cuban cigar, lit it up, blew some smoke out and they drove off. I then pulled myself together the best I could for now, and went home never to see him or the Swedish jewellers thieves again, or so I thought. Last I knew they'd opened a club in Spain and one in Morocco called 'Diamonds'. A bit ironic but fair play to them. I did go over there once or twice after I'd met up with them over here in England in Bagley's night club when they had invited me out there. I was also invited back to Ibiza from time to time to see and met a few other old faces who'd found refuge from the criminal system while they were out there for, now.

So the moral of the story is, I was left with 10 large and wet pants and no debt and no more circus. I'd paid Mr B off, and no one found out I never killed the fella. Well, a few people did but they weren't too bothered nor were the other firms. He was out the way and that's what they wanted, whether by me or whoever. It didn't matter to them. Maybe for a reason unknown to me as well but I'll never know.

It just seems weird how things panned out. I feel sorry for the people he's left behind. I've learned I'll always be an addict to cocaine, but it's the life I led back then that I was more addicted to. The life back then wasn't for me as I found out the hard way. I'd go over and over it in my head every day and believe me I wouldn't recommend it to any one else. If the stress don't kill you someone else might.

"Oh how the mighty fall" That's a good saying, eh? I did see Mr B in the club now and then. Now he walks with a limp. Someone must have got to him too. There's always someone bigger and better that wants to catch up with ya. That's if the police don't. I still see most of the firms and the faces but I don't get involved in the business no more. We just chat about old times and reminisce about the laughs we had until things got out of hand. It's nice to see them and then walk away. Back then there was no way out or walking away.

I did see old school again he was settled down and opened up a new Radio Station, he keeps himself to himself nowadays.

Today life's not too bad. I'm with the gorgeous Vivian, her two good children and mine and mum. I have a little baby and I try to do normal things. Life's too short to be looking over your shoulder all the time or biting the bullet.

And boys, you never know what card might be turned or when someone might throw in their ace card and before long you find yourself in the middle of things or an old favour might be called in and you have to make a little comeback every now and then, and then disappear like you've never existed.

THE END

BIG THANKS

Thanks to K for standing by me in prison and for giving me little H, and for driving us all mad.

Respect to all the people I met in and out of prison, those that helped me and helped to put this book together. Hope life's treating you well. A Special thanks to my Mum and Dad. (My dad sadly passed away) And my Grandparents, especially my Nan who also passed away. My Brother and his family. Viv and her family. To Mr P and his family, Treeny and his family, mark and his family, Mr Adams and his family and to Old School, for their input and other faces that were men tuned with the story that was put around them.

ONE LINE'S NOT ENOUGH AND A THOUSAND IS TOO MANY!!